The
POWER
Is in the Patient

a TA/Gestalt Approach to Psychotherapy

The POWER Is in the Patient

a TA/Gestalt Approach to Psychotherapy

By

Robert L. Goulding, MD

Mary McClure Goulding, MSW

Edited by

Paul McCormick

TA PRESS
SAN FRANCISCO

Published by
TA Press, San Francisco
Distributed by
Transactional Publications
1772 Vallejo St.
San Francisco, CA 94123

Printed in the United States of America
Typeset by Smith-Allen, Inc., Castro Valley, California
Cover photo by David Bracher

Library of Congress Cataloging in Publication Data

Goulding, Robert L.   1917–
    The power is in the patient

    Bibliography: p.
    Includes index.
    1. Transactional analysis. I. Goulding, Mary
McClure, 1925–   joint author. II. McCormick,
Paul, 1925–   III. Title.
RC489.T7G68   616.8'914   78–25604
ISBN 0–89489–002–6

We dedicate this book to
Paul McCormick
with love and thanks.

The International Transactional Analysis Association (ITAA)

The International Transactional Analysis Association (1772 Vallejo St., San Francisco, CA 94123) is a nonprofit educational corporation of about 10,000 members, 1,700 of them from 42 countries other than the USA. Its purpose is to serve the membership, and others, in the application and development of transactional analysis (TA), originated by Eric Berne, MD.

In the late 1950s and throughout the 60s Dr. Berne and his colleagues evolved TA as a comprehensive system for group and individual psychotherapy, for personal growth and behavior change, and for the improvement of human relations generally. The ITAA, founded in 1964 as an outgrowth of Dr. Berne's weekly San Francisco Social Psychiatry Seminars, includes clinicians in all the psychotherapeutic and counseling arts, and professionals from many other fields, including business, education, religion, and health care.

Membership levels range from Associate Regular to Certified, which includes Clinical and Special Fields (trained appliers of TA who have passed written and oral examinations). Teaching Membership authorizes a person to train and supervise candidates for certified membership.

An ITAA directory designates all who have been certified as transactional analysts.

Contents

Editor's Preface

When Morton Lieberman, Irvin Yalom, and Matthew Miles saw the results of the 17 treatment groups they studied for their book, *Encounter Groups: First Facts (1973)*, they were dismayed. Sixteen of the 206 group members who started ended as psychiatric casualities. Seventeen other members also changed for the worse, although less seriously so; 78 did not change at all; 27 dropped out; and only 68 improved, 40 of these only "moderately." A control group of about the same number, untreated, suffered no casualties. One of the conclusions the researchers had to draw was that group treatment can be dangerous.

Far and away the most productive of the 17 groups was the one led by Robert L. Goulding. Of the 12 persons who started with him, 10 changed positively, five of them more than "moderately," one remained unchanged, one dropped out, and none was a casualty.

The researchers studied the characteristics of the most successful group leaders and found that they had the following in common: a) they were only moderate in their use of "emotional stimulation" (they did not seduce the clients with charisma); b) they rated high in "caring"; c) they stressed "meaning-attribution" (they offered explanations of what they observed, and information on how to change); and d) they were only moderate in "executive function" (their use of structured exercises, and of "group management.") The method of treatment (whether psychoanalytic, gestaltist, psychodramatic, etc.) was less significant than the characteristics of the treaters.

Bob Goulding's explanation of why he did so well: "I made contracts for change, and took them seriously. The 10 who changed accomplished what they contracted to accomplish."

Bob does not hesitate to take credit for his effectiveness as a therapist, but he puts most of the credit on the one who makes the changes, the client. He is also convinced, though, that his understanding of psychotherapeutic theory, his ability to explain it to clients, and to have them experience it in their bones and guts as well as their heads, are crucial.

His cotherapist (and wife), Mary McClure Goulding, is similarly impressive as a treater. She is as tough as Bob in negotiating clear contracts with measurable goals, and in confronting clients who stop themselves from reaching those goals. Bob and Mary in action are a marvel to watch. To be treated by them is an inspiration.

About as casual appearing a couple as you could imagine psychotherapists to be (they sometimes look like they have just climbed out of a swimming pool to come straight to group—and they have), they quickly convince you that they know what they're about.

I saw Bob at the start of a treatment marathon tell a newcomer, a probation officer, that he might as well leave right now if he was going to hold others in the group responsible for his being "unable to do anything for myself here in front of people from my own office." The man did not even blink at Bob's remark. "Oh," he said. "Then I'll stay—and be responsible for myself." He did, and was.

Mary's intuitive gifts seem preternatural. She somehow senses clients' early scenes, when they might have made some grossly self-defeating decisions, and urges them to snap back to a reexperiencing of whatever it was they have not yet resolved—the better to redecide now.

Mary: "You look like a little boy whose daddy just broke his promise to take you to the circus."

Client: "Huh? That's exactly what he did when I was five. I'll never get over it." (But within 20 minutes he had.)

Mary comes up with these every marathon.

John McNeel, a clinical psychologist, wrote his doctoral dissertation (1975) on Bob and Mary's work. He studied in depth the procedures and effects of one of their marathons, with 15 clients being treated. All of them made important, and enduring, redecisions for themselves.

> ...[the marathon] had a profound effect on the lives of 15 people .... [as] substantiated by statistical fact, biographical data, and personal witness. The precise causes of this profound change may never be known ... [but] it is possible to make some educated guesses.... One predominant, yet unmeasurable factor ... was the sheer weight of the attractiveness of the personalities of the therapists.... Central to [their] ... theory of redecision therapy is the concept of [personal] responsibility and the importance placed upon discovering the early injunction-decision complex. But even these ... specifics become a vortex around which many other techniques and theoretical issues cluster. It seems that change cannot be assigned to any one particular as much as to the entire combination of elements. (Ibid., pp. 134-135)

McNeel identified three main kinds of work in the Gouldings' therapy: contracting for change, clarifying impasses, and redeciding (ibid., p. 133); and at least seven elements of that work (ibid., p. 115):

1. Emphasizing the client's power and personal responsibility for wanted change.

2. Creating a nurturing, protective environment for change.

3. The leaders' own modeling behavior, as example setting; especially their acceptance of themselves, and their enthusiasm for life.

4. Separating reality from client myths about self and others.

5. Confronting incongruity, especially between the verbal and the nonverbal (words vs. body language).

6. Using specific techniques such as game analysis, two-chair dialoguing, bringing the past into the present by use of fantasy, saying good-bye to the past, voicing hunches and intuitions, playing back on the tape recorder what the client said; etc.

7. Setting few but definite limits; for example, the no-gossip rule (no talking "about" someone, but only directly "to" the person, either in fact or in fantasy); and the time-limit rule (stopping at the hour contracted for, so clients will make best use of the time allotted.)

Explanations of why and how the Gouldings developed or adopted these procedures occur throughout this book. It is in effect a step by step description of the growth of a therapeutic system, told by a pair of master therapists who are still learning, still creating. None of it is their last word, I am sure, and none of it should be construed as the only way to do what they do. In chapter eight, for example, "Grass, Gobbledygook, and *Real* Groovin'," their work with "Joe" illustrates that back then they believed as Eric Berne did that providing "bull's-eye" information (information apparently accepted simultaneously by all three of the client's ego states, Parent, Adult, and Child) is the best way to facilitate change. As Joe *remembered* his childhood experience, they gave him bull's-eye observations, drawing his life script matrix on the board. Convincing stuff, they believed, as the client seemed to be impressed by all of it.

Now, Bob and Mary say, they would ask the man to enter the scene as the child he was, and discover his own information. He would probably have made his redecision then and there, in that scene, rather than in the months following the marathon.

Perhaps the most important of the Gouldings' contributions are: their assertive techniques for negotiating treatment contracts, so that they have leverage for advancing the clients toward the clients', not the therapists', goals; their classification of the destructive injunctions parents issue to their children; their recognition of the importance of the offspring's decision to go along with an injunction, as distinguished from the mere issuance of it; the development of combined TA and gestalt techniques to regress the client to that Child ego state in which a self-defeating decision was made, so that a redecision may be made in the same state, and thus be more likely to endure; their awareness of the three degrees of impasses, necessary knowledge for conflict-resolution work that lasts; their treatment of phobias, combining TA, gestalt, and desensitization techniques; and their combined treatment/training programs for psychotherapists.

These are considerable contributions.

Oh, yes. For the answer to why, on the cover, a picture of Bob fishing in his pond at Mount Madonna, see chapter one.

Paul McCormick

Acknowledgments

I have many acknowledgments to make, over the years, for my professional growth . . . Eric Berne, Fritz Perls, Jim Simkin, and many others about whom I say more in this book.

I want most to remember William Harris, MD, Veterans Administration Hospital, Perry Point, Maryland, and Wendell Muncie, MD, of Baltimore, Maryland. To both of them I owe my thanks for helping me to change from a humdrum psychiatrist to an innovative psychotherapist.

Robert L. Goulding, MD

This is a book about transactional analysis. Therefore it is only fitting that I thank my ancestors. Great-grandmother Matthews made special salves, slept one night in Lincoln's home, and told about her people, who were pioneers. Great-grandfather Ehman was the world's finest mantel carver, so I believed. Great-grandfather Burkhardt actually carved the Cardiff giant for P. T. Barnum. Grandfather Burkhardt, dentist, athlete, and storyteller, could make even dentistry wonderfully exciting. Grandfather McClure, banker, told of soldiers returning from the Civil War, and many stories of family. So did my Aunts Jessie, Marjorie, and Ethel McClure. To all of them I acknowledge the power of their message—life is exciting, and we in our family work successfully. I never heard a "poor us" tale.

My mother, Bertha Burkhardt McClure, insisted from the time I was five years old that I would grow up to be famous. She hoped I'd write the great American novel of our generation. Probably I owe her most. And yet my father, Leslie W. McClure, was the model who "showed me how." He was editor and publisher of the *Barrington Review*, a weekly newspaper that was well-written and free of typographical errors. I compared it proudly to the only newspaper I considered to be its competitor, the *Chicago Tribune*. Wholeheartedly I thank my parents.

Those are the counterinjunctions. The injunction, decision, and redecision:

To be a girl was once a blight
Firstborn and ugly
Yet they loved well
And gave a boy's nickname
Four sisters followed
With no one ever
To carry our lovely Scottish name
Into the future.

I watched man's world and vowed I'd prove
I should have been
I proved
And now
Surprising even me
I am pleased I am a woman.

Mary McClure Goulding

We both thank our sons and daughters, who enrich our lives: Margee Goulding Bennett, Kathleen Goulding Callahan, Roberta Goulding Brunet, Philip Goulding, Harry Goulding, Kelley Goulding, Robert L. Goulding, Jr., David (Tony) Edwards, Karen Edwards Lindblom, and Claudia Edwards.

All of the participants of our workshops and marathons taught us as we taught them. They are part of our larger family. Thanks to all of them.

A special thanks to Paul McCormick, our long-time friend, coenthusiast of jazz, coresearcher, and editor of this book—without whom it would never have been published.

R.L.G. and M.M.G.

1   *How to Catch Fish*   —R.L.G.

In 1948 I moved to North Dakota, first to do a locum tenens for an old friend, but then to stay. I worked hard to establish with him a growing general practice, and to satisfy the health needs of a population of 8,000, spread over 60,000 square miles. One day in late spring a banker friend, Don Stewart, said to me, "Doc, you're working too hard. You need to go fishing."

"Hell, Don," I replied, "all the fishing I ever did was drop worms in the East River in New York when I was 6, cast a piece of broom stick down my uncle's driveway when I was 10, and get skunked in Madison's Lake Mendota when I was 18. I don't know *how* to fish."

"I'm a good fly fisherman," Don said. "I'll teach you. Let's drive down to Sand Creek in Wyoming this weekend and catch us some trout."

So I went fishing. True to my prediction, I caught no fish, but I did learn something, and over the next 20 years, until Don died, he and I went fishing nearly every year—in Yellowstone, up near Glacier, in North and South Dakota, in Alligator Lake in Florida, in the Indian River in Florida, and a few other places. I learned about all there was to know about trout fishing—about flies, how to tie them, how to use them on a leader, how to tie a tapered leader, what kind of a rod to use, what kind of

First told at the end of a marathon led by Bob and Mary in 1970.

1

casting line to use; how to wade; how to use dry flies up-stream from the wading position, how to use wet flies, how to quarter in a large stream like the Yellowstone or Madison, how to cast into the wind. I learned how to look for rises, how to use Polaroid glasses to see the fish rising, how to treat floating line and keep it floating, how not to give other fishermen secret information, how to worm theirs out of them (although *worm* is not an OK word among purist fly fishermen) and how, sometimes, not to be purist when hungry and the only food is the stream's uncaught fish that are not taking flies. I learned how to get *all* my double-tapered lines out when necessary, and I could usually drop my fly in a tin cup no matter what the wind, at almost any reasonable distance, without slapping the water on the cast; and to lift up gently so not to frighten the wary trout. I learned how to avoid slapping the water on the back cast, and how to avoid snagging the trees or grass behind me. I learned how to avoid showing my shadow when scrambling along an unwadeable, narrow channel, to keep the trout from seeing me.

I learned a lot. I suppose I caught a few more fish than the untutored, but with all my knowledge, I really never caught many fish. In time my family and my friends would greet me on my return from Yellowstone, or Spearfish Canyon, or Big Bend, Montana, with "Well, Dad [or Doc], how many did you catch this time? Ha, ha, ha." Don had usually caught about 10 to my one. I began to get lots of strokes for not catching fish—and to laugh myself, but self-defeatingly.

Once my three-year-old son, an adult friend of mine, and I went to a dam to catch crappies, and my son carried home the news, "I catched three fish and Al one fish and Daddy no fish. Ha, ha, ha."

And so it went. In 1967 Don died, and I quit going fishing, because the real fun for me had been the companionship, and the camping, and the talk about ethics and morality (profound stuff, like "a staff prick has no conscience"), and fantasies about a magic island of peace and brotherhood we would start some day, with no laws, no restrictions except the Golden Rule—no fascists, no communists, just autonomous individuals not hurting the person or property of others.

The fun was in frying the fish, drinking the whiskey late at night, talking as the fire burned out, getting up at dawn, and fishing until the tourists came; and then lying on our backs in the sun, watching the birds fly by, listening to the loons, admiring a majestic moose drinking in the Madison River. (Those were good days, Don, and I regret you are not here now, although I have said my goodbyes, and have mourned for you, my friend, and for me. They never knew what a great man you were, although I knew, and somewhere down deep inside, you knew.)

And so I quit fishing, until the summer of 1969, when my two boys, Phil and Harry, suggested that once again we go, the three of us. That sounded great to me, and we made our plans.

"But this time," I exclaimed, "this year I am going to catch my share of the fish."

"OK, Dad," they said, "we'll catch 'em, you cook 'em—ha, ha, ha."

"No sir," said I, "I have redecided. I am catching my limit every day! No question about it. I have decided!"

This was in line with the work that Mary and I were doing on *redecisions*. Many of us, as youngsters, learned how to survive, and how to get along, by agreeing with the crazy demands placed on us. But we then let that early, irrational (for now) decision run our lives. I was aware that, somehow, I had decided not to catch fish, and although I was not in touch with all the ramifications of that decision, I knew I had to change it if I were to bring home the fish. At that time, too, I was almost bankrupt following a disastrous investment in a syndicate, after 20 years of successful general and psychiatric practice, and I had a hunch that my fishing and finances were somehow hooked to the same self-defeating early decision—obvious now, but not then.

So, we made our plans to go for the two weeks between Labor Day and the Monterey Jazz Festival. I notified my associates, and stopped by to see my aged mother, to let her know I would not be seeing her for a few weeks, and that I was going fishing.

"Oh, Bob, you're impossible!" she exclaimed. "You never catch any fish!"

Then I heard the connections.

"You can't fish, ha, ha." —("I guess I can't.")

"You haven't time for fun."—("I guess I haven't.")

"That's childish. You've got to take care of things." —("I guess so.")

"You don't know a thing about money."—("I guess not.")

"So work harder."—("Yeah.")

A whole series of injunctions that I had decided to go along with: Don't be a child; don't have fun; don't make money; don't catch fish. But work. And with your luck, you'd better work hard.

I knew then that I was about to change my life—to catch fish, to have fun, to have time for me, to enjoy the things I wanted. And not lose friends, lose money, lose fish, almost anything, as I had done. No more, no more, no more. I had made my decision: "I am going to catch fish!"

So, on the Friday before Labor Day of 1969 we started off for Yellowstone. This time we decided to go up 99 and fish the Sacramento above Shasta our first night out; and then cut across northeastern California and the tip of Oregon, and Nevada, and Idaho, hitting the Snake near Boise, then cutting across 20 to Idaho Falls—a new way, instead of 40 to Wells, then north. Mostly we wanted to check out some California water, because Yellowstone is a thousand miles from Carmel.

We were as far as the Bay Bridge when I remembered I had left my waders in the workshop house in Coyote, almost 100 miles back—my first slip in my new decision to catch fish.

How in hell can a man fish the fast waters of the Gibbon or the Truckee, or the cold waters of the Yellowstone, without waders? But wait, I thought, I can afford a new pair of waders, and, besides, I've always wanted a pair of felt-soled shoes like those I bought Don Stewart 15 years ago for his birthday, but never for me (another way of not catching fish?), even though I had slipped on the rocks dozens of times. (Who can catch fish sitting in the stream?) Aha, I thought, now I am beginning to see how I did not catch fish. I had fallen on my ass in the stream for lack of sure footing—I had fallen on my ass in the stock market for lack of understanding—I had fallen on my ass in some personal relations—all so I would not have fun, not enjoy, and not be free of worry. After all, if things were too good, how would I ever get myself to work hard? I'm seeing!

We arrived in Yellowstone on Labor Day evening. All the tourists were beginning to pack up, and by the next day the park would be empty except for us fishermen. I drove into West Yellowstone first thing in the morning, bought my felt-soled shoes and a pair of stocking waders, and went merrily back to Madison Junction to catch fish.

At dusk the night before, Phil and Harry had caught two or three little trout, wading right out, while I, alas, could wade only as far as my rolled-up pants would allow. Barefooted, I had gotten cold, cut my feet on the rocks, and caught no fish. But now, this morning, set with resolve, my hand steady, my legs covered, and my feet protected, I caught half a dozen rapidly, turning them back because we had all day to fish, and only a three-fish possession limit.

Suddenly I stopped getting strikes. Phil and Harry were still pulling them in. What, oh what was I doing wrong? I looked at my fly. Fly OK. I looked at my rod and my casting line. Rod OK, line floating. I looked at my leader. Aha! My nine-foot leader was now six feet, what with tying on flies and shortening it each time. Out with a new leader, off with the old (into my pocket to tie a taper to later), on with the new; a new fly tied, and back to catching fish. Hooray! I'm making my decision work.

Later all of us agreed the fish here had stopped striking. No more hatch, or fish bellies full, or sun warming up the surface—so we waded ashore. I started to suggest lying on the grass with a cold beer—but then remembered that the fun on this trip was to be in catching fish, not philosophizing over a beer. Off we went to the Gibbon, where the gorge is deep, the sun late, the water fast-moving, and the lunkies lurk in the gloomy depths, but rise lazily to swallow lurid lures. We drove to the picnic grounds on the shore of the Gibbon, a half mile of treacherous wading below the roaring falls—a half mile Stewart had always fought, while I lazily fished the shallows near the road, but catching no more than two or three 10-inchers. Don would return with two or three 18-to-20-inchers, and tales of the little ones he had put back.

"Not this time," saith the fisherman. "This time I, too, am going upstream, and catch some of those big ones."

Up we waded, three abreast, through the wide shallow run, catching a few little ones and turning them back. When we arrived at the tough part, Phil went up the right edge, I up the left, to fish the clefts and rocks; Harry agreed to follow to fish the pools 15 or 20 minutes later. By the time we reached sight of the falls, about 150 yards downstream of them, we had each slipped 18 inches of flipping trout into our creel, and had turned loose several under a foot. Then I got a granddaddy on the line. I had only a 3-lb.-test leader for this clear-cut water, so I had to play him not to lose him—and play him I did, over rocks and through deeps, getting soaked to my neck but holding on until it was a question of who would tire first. To survive was his decision, mine to catch fish. I won— 23 inches of plump, beautiful brown. As I netted him I heard a roar of approval and horns honking, and, looking up, I saw tourists lining the wall at the edge of Gibbon Falls, applauding my fight and my catch. I was getting strokes for catching fish, not for not catching them!

And so it went, for two weeks. Each time I fished and failed, I looked around to see what I was doing to stay with the old rather than the new decision. Sometimes I would have a black fly on, with the hatch gray—and no trout will strike at a floating black fly when all around it are floating gray flies. Sometimes I would be catching flies on trees, and spending my time in the trees where there are no fish, instead of in the water, where there are. Sometimes, if tired, I would splash on my retrieve, frightening the wary rainbows. So I would stop, rest, recover, and CATCH FISH. Sometimes I would forget, in the meadow, and let my shadow cross the quiet brook; and then I would approach from the east and drop my fly around the bend, and let it float gently, to tease the watching brown, until thrrp—I had him. What joy! I caught more fish in two weeks that I had in 20 years.

I am still catching fish. Recently I caught my limit in Kashmir, despite the poor advice of two guides about weights, and two flies on the line, and "Fish here, sahib."

This book is to tell you how to catch fish, whatever your fish are. It is for you, therapist, to improve your skills, and you, analyst, to show you a fresh dimension. It is for you, Marion Federal Penitentiary community, and for you, Wall Street banker, to show you how to enjoy, no matter what your confines are.

It is also for me, to help me live out my redecision.

. . . the phantom ideal goal of group therapy—the complete cure of every patient in one session. Eric Berne (1975, p. 459)

Eric Berne was my friend, and my first teacher in transactional analysis, which he originated. I remember fondly many meetings over the years—from playing poker in the mid-1950s, to sitting beside him as president of the Golden Gate Group Psychotherapy Society when he gave his last speech at the annual meeting, to being turned away when I went to see him the Sunday before he died, and feeling that my friend, with whom I had fought bitterly at times, no longer saw me as his friend, or so I thought.

Eric's stated position was that we could cure patients; that it was at least theoretically possible to cure them in one session; and that we should look for ways to do so. Beneath that overt confidence he was not all that optimistic. In *Games People Play* (1964, p. 184) he expressed hope for individual members of mankind, but not for mankind in general. His own life, during the last year, was not a happy one, with his divorce not quite final when

First appeared in somewhat different form as "Comments," appended to "Four Books on Group Therapy: A Review," by Eric Berne, in *Group Psychotherapy and Group Function,* edited by Max Rosenbaum and Milton M. Berger, copyright 1975, by Basic Books, Inc., Publishers, New York. Used by permission.

he died. When Mary and I asked him to come have a drink with us to celebrate our engagement, he said, "I feel too sad about my own marriage to celebrate with anyone else."

Whatever his private expectations for patients were, he created around himself an environment of confidence that troubled people really could be cured—although I prefer to say that people really can cure themselves. Herein lay the greatest difference between Eric and me. From his last book:

> The electrode is the decisive challenge for the therapist. He, together with the patient's Adult, must neutralize it, so that the Child can get permission to live freely and react spontaneously, in the face of the parents' programing to the contrary, and their threats if he disobeys. This is difficult enough with milder controls, but if the injunction is a demand made by a witch or giant whose features are distorted with rage, whose voice smashes through all the defenses of the child's mind, and whose hand is ever ready to strike humiliation and terror into his face and head, it requires enormous therapeutic power. (1972, p. 116)

I see the power as being in the patient, not in the therapist, and that the therapist's real job is to *allow* the patient to find his own power, and to put that power to use in a service, not a disservice. Eric repeatedly wrote and spoke about the "scripting" of patients, of how parents inserted electrodes into children's heads (the electrode is the Child of the parent in the Parent ego state of the offspring's Child), of how injunctions were "locked in solidly," that the script *determined* a person's life plan, and so on. When I said to him, "Damn it, Eric, you disregard the autonomy of the individual, and that all of us have choices," his response was, "If your parents told you that you can get well when you are 37, after you have seen a psychiatrist, then you can get well."

On this we disagreed. I believed, and still believe, that people make whatever decisions they have to make as children to survive psychologically and physically, and that they can remake a decision or make a new one at any time, and thus change the course of their lives. Eric believed the power to be in the "cowboy," as he called our kind of therapist. I believe the power is in the person, and that the therapist's job is to create an environment in which that person can make new decisions in his life, and get out of his script—to live autonomously, responding to the new environment in a way appropriate for this time and place, not hanging onto old feelings from the past, and looking for reasons to justify them.

Nonetheless he was a great teacher, a great creator of new ideas, and, above all, a great listener. He taught me to listen in a way that nobody else could—not even Fritz Perls. I am still listening.

3 *In Memoriam* —M.M.G.

Eric Berne the humanitarian looked at our world and understood the meaning of despair. He discredited success at the expense of others (is it success to be promoted to commandant of a concentration camp?), hated injustice and war, and especially our involvement in Vietnam; and finally, no doubt despairingly, conceived of the "little fascist" in each of us to explain the "at least 2800 years" that humans have been "willing and eager corpse-counters" (Berne, 1972, p. 271).

Eric Berne is dead. He doesn't know that we continued to promote war in Vietnam and Cambodia and Laos; he doesn't know what we did in Chile.

In his memory I wish to include a stanza from "Abejas" ("Bees"), written by the beautiful Pablo Neruda, Chilean, winner of the Nobel Prize for Literature, who was among those massacred after the death of Allende.

> Qué voy a hacerle, yo nací
> cuando habían muerto los dioses
> y mi insufrible juventud
> siguió buscando entre las grietas:
> ése fué mi oficio y por eso
> me sentí tan abandonado
>
> What am I going to do? I was born
> after the gods had died
> and my unbearable youth

continued searching among the crevices:
that was my duty and that is why
I felt myself so abandoned.

First appeared in somewhat different form in *Transactional Analysis Journal*, 1975, 5(1), 82.

4   *To My Clients*   —M.M.G.

I am bored with pathology. I am excited by health. And growth.

Tell me your troubles, confusions, mistakes, hates, and I'll listen for as short a time as possible; therefore, I'll treat you as fast as I can. Tell me of your triumphs and I'll hear you out. And applaud every word. If you are considering killing yourself, know that you'd kill only you, and that I'd mourn less than 10 minutes since I have no investment in you dead. Alive, come tell me of your growth. If you're considering being crazy, know I'd still enjoy the part of you that stays sane. I'll yawn and write no papers about your craziness.

I am not interested in your sucking in my protection, permission, or potency. My potency is: I give me to be with you in health, in growth, so that you, too, will discard in boredom your pathology and celebrate yourself in health.

First appeared in somewhat different form in *Voices: The Art and Science of Psychotherapy,* copyright 1975, *11*(1), 77. Used by permission of the American Academy of Psychotherapists.

5 New Directions in Transactional Analysis: Creating an Environment for Redecision and Change —R.L.G.

In the past decade, group therapy techniques at the Western Institute for Group and Family Therapy have undergone a marked change. Our approach to treatment has evolved gradually over this 10-year period, although the roots of our theoretical and therapeutic orientation go back to our learning about transactional analysis from the late Eric Berne. Under Berne's tutelage, we became aware that each of our patients was actually three people, and that their behavior and feelings changed with remarkable rapidity, depending on which ego state was in control: One moment we were watching a frightened child, the next moment we were listening to a stern parent, and then, only seconds later, we were listening to a rational, realistic, problem-solving adult. We realized that our patients characteristically assumed one of these three identities, Parent, Child, or Adult, at various points of their transactions with others. Once we had acquired these insights, we became aware of the frequency with

First appeared in somewhat different form in *Progress in Group and Family Therapy*, C. J. Sager & H. S. Kaplan (Eds.), New York: Brunner/Mazel, 1972. Used by permission.

which our patients demonstrated the same kinds of feelings after a series of similar transactions; we learned to recognize the games they were playing. We saw that our patients' transactions and games were part of a larger plan, of a life script they had "written" as children, and which they were determined to follow to its perhaps tragic end. Thus it seemed to us that they also deliberately behaved in ways that reinforced and served to perpetuate their feelings of worthlessness, rage, alienation, etc., so that in time they began to feel that they had no choice but to kill themselves, or kill someone else, or run away, or escape by going crazy or withdrawing.

Once we had become familiar with the basic concepts of transactional analysis, we learned to analyze ego states, transactions between ego states, games, and scripts, on the assumption, held by Berne and his followers, that if our patients were made aware of their feeling and behavior patterns, they would be able to change them. It soon became apparent, however, that this approach was not effective in a sufficient number of cases, and we changed our therapeutic methods in the group: Obviously, it was not enough to sit around waiting for our patients to develop this awareness, waiting for them to change as they "worked through" whatever it was they were supposed to be working through. Instead, we began to work quickly and carefully to tease out the patient's feeling and behavior patterns, to confront him with an exact model of his games, rackets, etc., which could be drawn, illustrated, felt. At the same time, our basic therapeutic orientation underwent some modification: Specifically, we recognized the importance of the injunction and decision which underlay these patterns. We came to understand that the patient's script, his games, and rackets, served to support a particular injunction he had been given in childhood and the particular decision he had made as a result of that injunction. And, finally, we realized that although we could make the patient acutely aware of his feeling and behavior patterns, he would not be able to change those patterns until he made a new decision and so free himself from the injunction. Thus, in recent years, our efforts have focused on creating a therapeutic environment which is truly conducive to change, or more precisely, to the process of redecision—on an emotional, as well as a cognitive level—which must precede change.

The Conceptual Framework

The Injunction

We learned from Berne that certain kinds of behavior, certain kinds of feelings, are often preceded by certain kinds of parental messages. Berne called these parental messages "witch messages"; we refer to them as "injunctions," and consider the term "witch message" antitherapeutic. By definition the injunction is a message given to the child by the parent's internal Child, usually (but not always) without the awareness of the parent's Adult. In essence the message tells the child how he can achieve recognition; i.e., under what circumstances he can expect to receive strokes from Mother or Father.

There is some difference of opinion among transactional analysts as to the extent to which these messages may vary in content. Berne, Steiner, Karpman, and others who attended the San Francisco seminars, believed that there were many possibilities, depending on the exact words used. We believe that there are only a few injunctions, and that often they are never actually spoken; rather, they are inferred by the child from his parents' actions. The first five injunctions we picked up were *"Don't be,"* *"Don't be you,"* *"Don't be a child,"* *"Don't be grown up,"* and *"Don't be close."* Subsequently we identified two more—just plain *"Don't,"* and *"Don't make it";* and then we picked up still another—*"Don't be sane"* (or well).[1] Finally, although we are not yet certain of the frequency with which it occurs, we became aware of the injunction *"Don't be important."*[2] Another just added is *"Don't belong."*

With additional clinical experience, we recognized that these injunctions, which had been given to our patients when they were children by an irrational part of their parents, were, in fact, the real force behind the scripts they were in, and the games they played to support those scripts.

A depressed, suicidal woman of 44, who had done things to drive people away all her life, could relate her depression to the injunction not to be, which had been given to her as a child by her mother. The patient had been told over and over again that she alone was the cause of her mother's unhappiness; that if she hadn't been born, hadn't been conceived, mother could have gone to college, or would never have gotten married, or could have had a career in opera, or would not have developed hemorrhoids,

---

[1]Presumably, we would have picked up this injunction much sooner had we been seeing more psychotic patients. In recent years we have been working primarily with therapists who are candidates for training in transactional analysis. Consequently, we have lost touch with the psychotic segment of the patient population. Apparently, however, there are enough therapists around with serious problems so that in time we were able to pick up the "Don't be sane" injunction.

[2]This injunction was brought to our attention by Edward Frost, one of our trainees from the ministry.

etc. And what all this, together with all the nonverbal messages the mother sent out, added up to what was "Don't be." Even after 40 years, the patient continued to obey that injunction, continued to behave in ways that would heighten her feelings of worthlessness, and her sense of alienation. Thus she showed us how she added up the evidence of all the bad things that happened to her so that she would have enough bad feelings to support her depression. And when she couldn't find the evidence, she made bad things happen to her so that she could feel depressed. Or if she did not feel sufficiently depressed at a given moment, she would fantasize something in the past or the future to be depressed about; or, when all else failed, she would think about the war, the political situation, etc., and become pathologically depressed.

Because the injunction is reinforced by strokes given by the parent at the time he or she transmits the "message," the child comes to perceive failure to obey the injunction as a threat to psychological survival. These strokes, or units of recognition, may be positive or negative. Obviously, in the "Don't be" injunction, they are usually negative. But if no positive strokes are delivered, then negative strokes become very important: Children would rather be treated badly than completely ignored. Strokes may also be categorized as unconditional or conditional: Parents may love their children unconditionally, just for being; or they may love them just for doing things they approve of; or they may love them for both being and doing. Similarly, parents may dislike their children (or perhaps only one of them) just for existing; or the children may receive negative strokes only when they do something bad, and be ignored the rest of the time; or they may receive both unconditional and conditional negative strokes. Children who are given a "Don't be" injunction are often slapped and scolded by the parents just because they exist. As a general rule, however, the "Don't be" injunctions are implanted by conditional as well as unconditional negative strokes: The children will be slapped and scolded if they try to break the bars of the crib, bang their heads, throw their bottles around, spill milk, throw toys on the floor, etc. If, on the other hand, they are quiet, can be left alone in their rooms for long periods, don't get in anyone's way, don't "bug" anyone, they will be ignored. Thus, such children learn that the parents will give them strokes (i.e., recognition) for being bad and forget that they exist if they are good. And then they are in a quandary: If they are recognized, they hurt; but if they do nothing to deserve a spanking or scolding, and that's the only way they can attract the parents' attention, they are lonely—and loneliness is infinitely more painful. There is still another possibility: If the child is given an injunction to stay out of the way, and gets positive strokes for staying out of the way, he will begin to realize that he will be loved for not being there, and scolded if he is. And this type of situation, in which the parent actually gives the child warm, loving strokes when he or she obeys an injunction, however irrational, may have an even more noxious effect on the child's future development.

As a child, while his father was away in the war, the patient received a "Don't be you" (i.e., "Don't be a boy") injunction from his mother, who dressed him in girl's clothes, and then loved him for being a "girl." Furthermore, the mother really hated men, so that even the counterinjunction, which came from the mother's Parent, was "Be a girl." Thus, the patient saw no alternative but to decide to go along with the injunction. As long as he remained a boy, he wouldn't get strokes because mother didn't want "him," she wanted "her." Having made a decision to comply, he became depressed and in time began to gather reasons to knock himself off.

Given these data, one can predict the kind of life script the patient developed for himself: When he was first seen, the patient was a homosexual whose behavior might best be described as frenzied; in addition, he was depressed, suicidal, alcoholic, and blind. Over a two-year period, several therapists worked with him to extricate him from the "Don't be a boy" injunction and the early decision he had made as a result of that injunction, and to help him make a redecision about his maleness. At the end of those two years, the patient was no longer suicidal, but he was certainly not well, and he was still blind. At this point, the patient decided to undergo surgery to change his sex, discussed his problem with the staff at a university-affiliated hospital, and, after considerable effort, persuaded both the surgical team and the psychiatric team that such an operation was justified. Shortly after he started a course of hormonal treatments prior to surgery, the patient began to dress in women's clothes and work as a housekeeper. In addition, while he was receiving hormonal treatments, his blindness, which was central (vision was 20/800 peripherally), disappeared, and he/she no longer felt depressed. (Subsequently, both stages of surgery were completed, and for over two years the patient has been doing well, living and loving as a woman. She is now married and has two stepchildren.)

This case illustrates the power of the injunction, but it also serves to highlight an aspect of the injunction that has not received enough attention in the literature; namely, the trap the therapist may fall into if he allows the patient's contract to be influenced by his own convictions. Thus, if despite his stated goals, the patient persists in his determination to stick with the early injunction he was given, after considerable work has been done, the therapist would do well to reexamine and, possibly, to revise his own commitment to implement that contract.[3]

The Decision and Its Sequelae

Once we recognized the influence of the injunction, and were able to specify the various forms it might take, we became aware of another element, one that we think Berne and his close followers missed: If Mother said, from her irrational Child ego state, "Don't be," the child had to agree to make a *decision* not to be, if the injunction was to hold any power.

Many children get a "Don't be" injunction from a parent who doesn't want them, but only certain children decide not to be. Others respond differently; they decide to ignore their parent's message, regardless of the consequences. We are not sure why some children do not feel impelled to obey an injunction, but there are several possible explanations: Obviously, the other parent often plays a crucial role in such cases. To illustrate, if Mother says, from her crazy, irrational Child, "Don't be," but Father says, "Don't listen to her, she's nuts; she's mad at life, not at you," then in all probability the child will be able to get through his early years without deciding to kill himself someday. Similarly, if a father says "Don't grow

---

[3]Obviously, this would not apply to the suicidal patient.

up" to his sexy nine-year-old daughter, she may well decide to obey his injunction, to remain a little girl so that father will love her, unless her mother says, "Don't listen to him. It's OK for you to grow up; give him some time and he'll love you anyway. And even if he doesn't, it really won't be that important after you've grown up and left home."

There is a second possible explanation: The child may remain uncommitted to a parent's injunction, even when it is not countermanded by the other parent, if he is strong enough emotionally to recognize that his psychological survival does not really depend upon his parents, that he can get the recognition and support he needs from parent surrogates.

The point is that the child doesn't have to buy the injunction. And if he does buy it, he doesn't have to stay with it forever. Accordingly, we provide our patients with an opportunity to change their early decisions. At times, they may even make the same decision they did as children (except for the decision not to be), for although it may have had an adverse effect on early development, a redecision might now be considered relatively "unsafe." For example, the child who decides to obey the injunction "Don't be a child" often works hard from the time he is six years old to accomplish things, and is amply rewarded for his efforts, but isn't really enjoying life. In fact, this injunction frequently underlies the life script of the professional who undertakes further training in his spare time, who continues to strive for recognition as a grownup, and does not permit himself to enjoy childlike pleasures. Even when he is relaxing, he may be pushed by his internal Parent to "get off your rear end and get something done." He has two choices—to decide to have fun, be a child at times, and then be alert to the deprivation he feels, recognize its source, and look for strokes from people who are also interested in having fun. Or, second choice, he can decide to stay with the original decision of not being a child, and stop hassling himself about his unwillingness to have fun; and he can stop doing things like going into debt so that he can't afford fun, or stop fighting with his wife when it's time to have sex.

What needs to be emphasized is that the great majority of children do make an initial decision to go along with the injunction given them, although the effects of this decision may vary considerably, depending, of course, on the content of the injunction. For obvious reasons, the "Don't be" injunction would be expected to have the most serious implications. Thus if the child feels impelled to obey the "Don't be" injunction, then at some point in the young life, she or he may make one of the following decisions:

1. If things get too bad I'll kill myself.
2. I'll get you, even if it kills me.
3. I'll get you to kill me.
4. I'll show you, even if it kills me.

Other decisions can be made, of course. The above are listed by way of illustration. The point is that, whatever form it may take, once children have made such a decision, they have forfeited their autonomy. There is a good chance that they will remain stuck with the injunction, in a script that must support it.

Thus we saw repeatedly: An injunction from the Child ego state of the parent (or parent surrogate) had been followed by a decision made by the patient to go along with that injunction, after which the patient developed a set of bad feelings that were consistent with that decision; began to play games to maintain or support those bad feelings (the feelings we call rackets); began to collect those bad feelings and the bad things that happened, so that he or she could cash them in later for the suicide, or depression, or the anger or anxiety that the script called for.

The Games. The ways in which the games the patient plays serve to support the injunction and the script emerge clearly in the following clinical illustration:

> Joe, who was the oldest of several children, had been born before his mother was married, and had been given a "Don't be" injunction: If it weren't for him, the other kids would have enough to eat; and if it weren't for him she wouldn't have had to get married, and wouldn't have had all those kids in the first place. As might be expected, the injunction not to be had been reinforced by negative strokes. And so Joe learned very early in life that the way to get recognition was to do something bad, and the way to feel was depressed and sad; he decided that if things got too bad he could always knock himself off.
>
> At first he got recognition by getting his mother to scold him for spilling the milk, etc. And he began to equate being scolded with being loved. Thus he was motivated to start playing the game, as the patient often is, by his need to ensure his psychological survival.
>
> To trace the evolution of this process: first, he spilled the milk; second, he sent his mother the secret message, "Please scold me"; third, she complied; fourth, his mother's negative strokes evoked bad feelings, which he collected and cashed in for his first suicide attempt when he was only six. Fifth, while Joe was probably conscious of this whole procedure when he was a small child, in his data-processing Adult he was not aware of what his Child was doing. Consequently, as Joe grew up he continued

to play the game, "Kick Me," and, from his Child position, asked to be kicked (and loved) over and over again.

Thus, the requirements for a game, according to the late David Kupfer, one of my cotherapists, and me, are:

1. Ostensibly straight (usually Adult—Adult) transaction
2. Secret message
3. Response to secret message
4. Payoff of bad feelings
5. Entire series of ulterior transactions outside of Adult awareness (but not necessarily unconscious)

The Life Drama's First Act. To review: The person gets an injunction from his parent, which is reinforced by strokes (positive or negative, conditional or unconditional); he makes a decision around that injunction; and develops a script to support the injunction. Sometimes, however, the child has some kind of "first-act" experience, in the course of which he develops some bad feelings from the strokes he gets and the things that happen to him, but also gets some satisfaction from the strokes, and often, when young, some kind of reward for his bad feelings. As demonstrated below, when it occurs, this "first-act" sets the pattern for the feelings and modes of behavior that the child retains until (and if) he decides to change.

A patient came to our institute, depressed and suicidal, shortly after I had decided to give up my private practice to devote my time to teaching, training, and conducting workshops. She had been depressed on and off all her life, but in the last several years her depression had become acute; for some time now she had been suicidal, and had made two abortive attempts to kill herself. She attributed her depression to the fact that her husband had divorced her two years earlier and had since remarried. What she was really saying now, from her Child, was, "Please come back so that I can stop being depressed," although what she said out loud was, "How can I help being depressed when I don't have the man I love anymore?"

Because she had been a friend of the family, she wanted me to treat her. I explained why that would not be possible, and suggested that she see one of my associates. She agreed, but even after she had been in treatment for several months, she continued to feel acutely depressed. She had a new rationalization, however. When she came into the office and ran into me, she said, "How can I help being depressed when I don't have you as my therapist?"

And then one day when we met by chance in the reception room, I was struck that her behavior looked like a "first act" she might have experienced as a child. As soon as she saw me she said, "If you don't see me today, I'm going to kill myself." I warned her not to try to blackmail me: "If you feel suicidal, I'll arrange to have you admitted to the hospital, but I won't see you." At this point she began to cry like a child, and I asked her if she remembered the first time she didn't get her way, and cried until she did. She recalled that when she was five or six years old she had wanted a particular doll for Christmas. When she got the wrong doll she had cried and cried until her father finally went out, the day after Christmas, and got her the right one. Clearly then, she had experienced a "first act" in which being depressed and crying got her the goody she was looking for, at which point being depressed and crying acquired some magical power.[4] Apparently she had done the same thing over and over again with her husband until he finally refused to play his part. But even after he had divorced her and married someone else, she continued to believe that her depression had the power to bring him back. Indeed, it was only after she got in touch with the shame of carrying on this way that she was able to give up the first act, and to knock off her depression instead of herself.

The Rackets. The bad feelings, or rackets, that we hold onto, then, are those feelings, often copied from our parents, that we experienced and got rewards (strokes) for when we were little children. We subsequently came to believe that they had some magic power, which fit into the script or the first act in that they served to support the particular injunction we were given. A little child's bad feelings frequently serve an important function, of course: The young child, who is almost totally dependent on others, must use every possible means of attracting attention if his basic psychological and physiological needs are to be gratified. But the bad feelings that we hold onto, or play games to get, or use as an excuse to withdraw, that don't motivate us to take Adult action, are rackets.

One need only drive down any freeway with different people and watch their behavior to be convinced of the ubiquity of rackets. A few drivers can turn on their radios and listen to music while they go where they have to go, without permitting the behavior of other drivers, no mat-

---

[4]This episode was probably a screen memory, but it would still be considered a first act.

ter how provoking, to elicit bad feelings. But they are the exceptions. For the rest, some are in a state of fury throughout the trip; they get angry when other drivers tailgate, or cut in, or even when they come onto the freeway from a side access; some are so confused by the traffic and by the signs that they begin to feel disoriented; some are depressed by the traffic; some are frightened by all the kamikaze pilots; etc. The patterns are the same: They say, "The traffic is making me anxious today," but they are also anxious lying in bed thinking about the next day's traffic. Or they say, "Who wouldn't be depressed having to drive in this traffic every day?" but they never look for a house or apartment closer to their job, or try to find a job closer to home. Or they try to excuse their irrational anger on the grounds that, "Everyone in my family gets angry easily. It comes from having red hair" (gene theory); or "What's going on in the world makes me angry" (cosmopolitan theory); or "I have a lot of unconscious hostility" (pseudo-Freudian theory). The point is that that they are all refusing, in different ways, to assume responsibility for themselves, to exercise their autonomy. Instead they stay in the rackets their parents taught them, stay in their script or their first act; play games, or, if it becomes necessary, use fantasy to support the rackets and script.

A participant in one of our workshops can be actively involved in what he is doing then and there; or he can be anxious about what he will do when the workshop meets again; or he can be anxious about what the other people in the group thought of him at the last workshop; or he can even be anxious about what is happening in Vietnam, and the possibility that China might enter the war. Although he is probably not aware of it, his anxiety is a racket: He is using a bad feeling from his irrational Child as an excuse to withdraw.

We see, then, everyone is in the same bag to some extent. In fact, we rarely train a professional, even one who has had years of psychoanalysis, or gestalt therapy, or TA, or whatever, who doesn't still have some injunction, some script that he is still following. Thus, for example, the therapist who feels frustrated because his patients don't get well faster is probably doing something that prevents them from changing, or is setting goals for himself in the therapist-patient relationship that he won't live up to (*won't*, not *can't*), or he is actually letting the patient exercise some measure of control over his feelings by using techniques he knows will backfire; e.g., by telling the patient what to do and then being frustrated when (of course) he doesn't do it. Chances are that when this therapist was four, Daddy told him, in some way, to cure Mommy, and he is still trying to cure patients from his four-year-old position.

Therapeutic Innovations: Redecision

Precipitating Factors

As we developed our skills at putting these pieces together, we realized that, frequently, just when the group was ready to deal with some important point the time would be up, and we would have to send everyone home so that we could get to the next group. And so we determined to increase the time traditionally allotted to a single group treatment session. At first, we experimented with the three-hour group, then the six-hour group, the twelve-hour group, and finally we tried the weekend marathon, which proved the most effective of all. It seemed to us, and it also seemed to them, that when our patients worked together continuously for three days, they often accomplished as much as they had in six months of regularly scheduled therapy sessions. We then began to hold weekend marathons, not only for our already existing groups, but also for other patients, our own and others'. We were impressed by how much more they were able to learn about themselves, about the injunction, their early decision and its consequences; impressed that once they became aware of the origins of their feelings and behavior, they frequently began to stop playing their most serious games. On the other hand, we had to face the fact that although our patients might be able to stop playing their serious games, and were no longer determined to pursue a life plan that would end in suicide or homicide, they were not prepared to give up their entire script, or all their rackets and games. They often found new ways to maintain their rackets; they often continued to play some other less serious game (e.g., the alcoholic might stop drinking only to start playing "Debtor").

Apparently, no matter how favorable their initial response to the weekend marathon was, our patients failed to progress beyond a certain point in therapy. As we became increasingly aware of what gestalt therapists call "the impasse," we realized that it related to the danger of giving up the injunction and the decision: Usually, a patient reached an impasse in his treatment because he was listening to the early injunction given him by his parent, and facing the fantasied threat of the parent's rage if he changed his original decision to go along with that injunction. In other words, he equated giving up his early decision with the loss of the love and nurturing he was getting, or expected to get if he was a good boy and did what Mother or Father wanted. Thus we were presented with clinical evidence in support of our observation, noted earlier, that the power of the injunction lies in the fact that it carries with it the threat that love (and/or recognition) will be withdrawn, or never offered, unless the patient goes along with it. Even when the parents had been dead for many years, the patient continued to behave as if they would come back and love him, or love him in the afterlife, provided he stayed with the injunction and the decision. It was this fantasied threat of psychological retailiation, then, that seemed to account for the impasse our patients reached, and which precluded their further progress in treatment.

At about this time we were exposed to the gestalt methods used by Fritz Perls (1969, 1969) and James Simkin (1972) and to Virginia Satir's (1964) family methods, and over a 10-year period we experimented with these and other treatment techniques. We found that for us no single traditional approach to treatment—traditional Berne, traditional Perls, or whatever—really created an environment for change; i.e., an environment that would foster the resolution of the impasse as a prerequisite for change. On the other hand, we recognized the potential effectiveness of an eclectic approach of various elements drawn from each of these sources. Thus we began to develop a distinctive style of therapy that combined the traditional techniques, developed from our early indoctrination in psychoanalysis and the psychodynamics of behavior, with Berne's TA and my own variations on TA (including stroking for change and not stroking for nonchange), with Perls' and Simkin's gestalt methods, Satir's family techniques, and occasionally some psychodrama. In short, we sought to combine traditional techniques that foster cognitive awareness with techniques that foster emotional awareness: Over weekends of intensive therapy we taught the patient the TA approach, and worked with him concurrently in the gestalt approach so that he could get through his impasse by making a redecision. Only then did he really begin to change, to stop playing games, to stop maintaining his rackets, to stop following his life script—and to become more autonomous.

Treatment Techniques

We use several methods to help the patient reach a redecision. Often redecision is reached when the nuclear family is recreated, as Satir does with her sculpting, or when the patient engages in a fantasied dialogue with his parent:

A 20-year-old girl with a "Don't grow up" injunction was able to fantasy a dialogue with her father, in the course of which she told him, "I'm not going to stay a baby for you." Then, in the manner of patients who are in gestalt therapy, she told each member of her group in turn, "I'm not going to stay a baby." And now there was a dramatic change in her appearance: She took her hands away from the front of her crotch, she straightened her shoulders, her voice dropped almost an octave, she pushed her breasts out, sucked her abdomen in, and started moving her hips seductively. In short, she looked like a 20-year-old woman instead of a nine-year-old girl—and felt the change deep in her guts.

Often the redecision can be reached by Melges' method of allowing the patient to fantasy about his future, to predict where he will be 10 years from now if he continues in his present life script, and where he will be 10 years from now if he changes. He may then make a redecision based on the projection of his future.

Thus, at this stage in our professional development, we work quickly and intensively to get to the early injunction and decision, and create an environment for change, an environment in which the patient will learn to stop playing games to support his rackets which, in turn, provide him with the evidence he needs to stay in his life script. In essence, of course, all TA therapists share these goals. We don't expect the patient to give up his games just because he has become aware of the fact that he's been playing games, or because he's been told they're neurotic; and we realize that he won't expect to give them up because they make him feel bad. Rather, we create a therapeutic climate in which the patient can make a new decision regarding the injunction that underlies his life script. Once he has made this redecision, his games and rackets become obsolete. There is no need for him to play "Kick Me" if he isn't going to add up the kicks and try to cash them in for a free suicide—if, in short, he has made a new decision surrounding the "Don't be" injunction he was given as a child. He has no reason to get into an uproar with his wife in order not to be close, if he has made a new decision not to go along with his parent's "Don't be close" injunction. And if, on the other hand, he has decided to stick with that injunction, if his uncontaminated Adult has made a decision not to be close, he does not need to provoke an argument to avoid closeness.

Redecision versus the counterinjunction. Some of the more orthodox TA therapists may take the position that the patient can only give up the injunction, which comes from the parent's Child, if he obeys the counterinjunction, which comes from the parent's Parent. Thus if the patient received a "Don't be" from his parent's Child, but his parent's Parent said "Work hard, succeed," the patient would be "cured" if he decided to switch to the counterinjunction. In addition, a number of TA therapists, Schiff and Steiner, in particular, often treat from their Parent, or, more precisely, assume the role of the patient's "good" parent. Thus Schiff (1970) encourages her schizophrenic patients to divorce their real parents completely, and she reparents them in an attempt to provide them with the consistent, rational parents they never had.

Apparently Schiff's method has been successful, but we question its therapeutic value over the long term. If the patient recognizes that he made the wrong decision at some point in his early life because it seemed to be the only decision he could make at the time, then he can change that decision. Instead of trying to change the content of the injunction, which, in a sense, has become part of the patient's neurophysiology, he can redecide not to listen, to act on his own. If in pursuit of autonomy, why stop listening to the injunction of one parent only to begin listening to the injunction of another parent, who happens to be the therapist? Steiner (1967) believes that if a suicidal patient gets a "Don't jump" injunction from his therapist when he gets to the edge of the Golden Gate Bridge he will hear the therapist saying "Don't jump," and so will not. I would suggest that if the patient makes a new decision regarding the "Don't be" injunction he was given, if he redecides, on his own, not to kill himself, he will not get to the edge of the bridge in the first place.

The injunction versus the "witch message." If TA therapists think of the patient as a victim of his parents, and believe that the best way to get the patient to give up the injunction is to encourage him to deny his parents, they might conceive of, and refer to the injunction as the witch message. One TA therapist, in fact, used to have his patients dance around a circle singing "Ding Dong the Witch is Dead," at the conclusion of each marathon.

This technique sounds very exciting and like fun. The trouble is that it may not allow the patient really to say good-bye to the past. It can help him to hold onto his image of his mother and father as witches, and to maintain his negative feelings toward his parents. The patient cannot give up his injunction until he lets his parents go; he cannot function autonomously until he stops shifting the responsibility for his behavior onto his parents.

The patient will have reached an important point in his treatment when he recognizes that his parents were real people who suffered their own hurts and disappointments. For then he will begin to forgive them, not in a maudlin way, but as a result of his deep gut recognition that his parents were not witches or monsters; they may have been just two people trying to get along, hurting, and passing on some of the hurts—what Fanita English calls the hot potato (1969).

The contract. As is well known, the contract, as that term is used in transactional analysis, refers to the agreement the therapist makes with the patient to work on the patient's goals. In practice, the contract goals, as formulated by the patient, provide us with data that are crucial to the success of our therapeutic efforts. Thus we ask the patient what he wants to achieve now, or today, or this week, or in the next eight weeks. Then we look for the injunction, the script or first act, the early decision, the games, and the rackets—in short, we look for all the ways in which the patient denies his autonomy.

We listen to the patient's words—*try, can't, want, should, ought to, why-because*—all the ways he has of saying *won't*, of copping out. And now we ask him to get in touch with the real power of the *won't:* If he's been saying, "I want to quit smoking," for example, we ask him to say, "I *won't* quit smoking," instead. And then we ask him to fantasy where he will be in 5 years, or 10 years, or 15 years, if he continues to smoke, and let him realize the full implications of his life pattern. We let him feel enough organismic shame or disgust, to use Simkin's term, so that at that moment he will make a redecision, feel the change in his guts, feel the flood of relief of having made a real decision to grow, or play, or live.

What we do, then, is to work quickly to put the patient in touch with himself, to make him aware of himself, of the lack of congruence between what he thinks and what he feels, the lack of congruence between what he says and his behavior; we lead him to see how he maintains the same kinds of feelings, regardless of the situation, how he sets things up so that he can stay in the bad feelings that support the injunction and the script he is in, and thus rob himself of his own autonomy. We do not allow him to talk about his past relationship with his mother or father; we ask him to sit in a chair facing one or the other parent, and talk to them now. We ask him to take both parts, and frequently in this way he is able to get to the roots of the basic core position in life which he has held onto for many years.

A 40-year-old woman was able to find all sorts of things to feel guilty about, until she had collected enough guilt to seriously consider knocking herself off. We asked her to be 35 ("What do you feel guilty about now?"); then 30, then 25, then 20, etc. At 40, she felt guilty about driving her husband away; at 35 she was guilty about how she was raising her children; at 30 she felt guilty because she did not have orgasms; at 25 she felt guilty about having become pregnant at 20, before she was married; at 20, she felt guilty about being pregnant; at 15 she felt guilty about not getting her household chores and homework done; at 10 she felt guilty about masturbating; at 5 she felt guilty every time she made too much noise, or did something her parents did not like.

Finally, we asked her to be a newborn baby: What did she feel guilty about now? She didn't know, so we asked her to put herself in her mother's skin and tell Carol (the patient) what was wrong with her. As her mother (Edna), she told herself that all her (Edna's) troubles started when she became pregnant with Carol, that her whole lousy life was Carol's fault, that it was Carol's fault that she had been conceived. When Carol made Edna say this, she stopped playing the part of her mother, and started to laugh. "That's silly," she said, moving back to her own chair. "You're not blaming me for my own conception. You're nuts, and I'll be damned if I'm going to feel guilty about being alive anymore." At that point, then, she had more than Adult cognition of the reason she continued in her rackets. Deep down she felt that she was really OK.

This is a far cry from shouting "You're OK" at patients; or from looking carefully for the right words to give patients. In this case, the patient gave herself the words, which put her in touch with the incongruity of her position. Once she recognized this incongruity, she could begin to break loose from her old life pattern by checking herself whenever she did something, or felt something, or behaved in some way that fit that pattern. No one I know has worked through an impasse and then become forever happy, but the enthusiasm and excitement the patient feels at the moment of breakthrough, and shares with the group, are unique. Moreover, these feelings give the patient a new frame of reference for his everyday activities. His feelings and behavior are no longer predetermined by his overwhelming sense of guilt. Then, having acquired a new sense of his own worth, the patient can get out of his old script.

For instance, Carol was really in a Cinderella script: She had been scrubbing the hearth, waiting for her fairy godmother to come and release her, and feeling guilty and depressed while she waited. From time to time she had entered treatment, and had briefly given up her mother's injunction to drop dead, and the script, but only to obey the counterinjunction, "Work hard; scrub the hearth": thus, if she was a good girl, and worked hard in therapy, then the therapist would magically reward her with a coach and four, and she could give up her script. The trouble with fairy tales is that the writers were crooks: they took a real life situation and tacked on a phony ending; little girls who read fairy tales and wait for the magic prince to get them out of the set are doomed to disappointment.

The real success in therapy comes when the patient is able to work through an impasse, to get on the other side by both redeciding and feeling the redecision. Making what Simkin calls an "intention" to change is not the same as changing. The patient who makes a redecision to enjoy life, or to live, or to be close makes it at the moment that he feels it in his bones and guts, at the moment he feels the real joy of being free. Only then can he really let go of his injunctions and counterinjunctions, his games, his rackets, and his script.

The function of the group. When Carol stopped feeling guilty, and made a redecision to live, and to take positive steps to implement that redecision, she got strokes from the rest of the group for her work. Thus, she became aware of the fact that the rewards she could expect for living surpassed the rewards she had been getting for being depressed. She then proceeded to establish a different life style for herself.

The group is used to provide an encounter experience for the working patient. We no longer sit by and wait for someone to say something; we take a strong lead. We do a great deal of one-to-one work in the group, and ask other patients to intervene when they have something to say. We do not use encounter tricks, but use the group to reinforce the patient's redecision. For example, it will be recalled that we asked a young patient to tell each member of the group that she was no longer a baby. In contrast to the patient's parent, the group gives the patient strokes for change; thus it is a force for change.

Conclusion

To help clarify the therapeutic concepts and innovations described above, here is a detailed account of a weekend group marathon session. To summarize our philosophy: We believe that change must occur on an emotional level, but that it is facilitated by cognition. We use ourselves to facilitate change, but not as new parents. If the patient chooses to cast us in the role of parents, we need to make sure that he will not set up his old games with new referents. Thus autonomy for the patient is our goal. We believe that the techniques used in TA therapy to foster cognition, combined with the guts work of gestalt therapy, are the best way to reach that goal.

ANNOTATED TRANSCRIPT OF A GROUP THERAPY WEEKEND MARATHON

The annotated transcript of a group therapy marathon, which follows, demonstrates in greater detail the clinical application of the theoretical concepts discussed above.

The following quotes focus on Tim, a 21-year-old patient who was seriously ill, and suicidal. Tim had been hospitalized previously for treatment of a drug (LSD)-induced psychosis, manifested by delusions, hallucinations, irrational and bizarre behavior, looseness of associations, flight of ideas, etc. He had been out of the hospital for about five weeks when he attended his first group meeting.

Initially, Tim's behavior was rather provocative, and the other members of the group cooperated in his attempt to maintain bad feelings about himself. However, once we diagrammed the moves of the "Kick Me" game he was playing, Tim agreed to stop (and, if he slipped, not to accept the payoff). Instead, he would get closer to the other members of the group. At the next two meetings, he did well in that he did not play any serious games, and participated, to some extent, in the work the others were doing. He was not working for himself, however. At this point we invited him to take part in a marathon. Tim accepted our invitation, but after the marathon started, he sat around silently for awhile and then proceeded to express some doubts about its value.

Tim: "Bob and Mary,[5] I'd like to . . . I came here to get something done. And it's not been getting done too much, and I'm not enjoying myself too much."
(*By saying "It's not been getting done too much," rather than "I'm not doing much," he's relinquished responsibility for what happens to him.*)
Mary: "What is it you still want to get done?"

---

[5]In general, we encourage patients to call us by our first names to counteract any tendency on their part to cast us in the role of "good" parents, who would tell them what to do, make decisions for them, etc.

Tim: "Um . . . I still want to decide to live for sure, and I don't really know how to ask you to help me do that. But I do want to do it." *(This is the first move toward a redecision.)*

Mary: "So you want to decide to live. And that you will go on living no matter what?"

Tim: "Yeah [*questioning note in his voice*]. Well, not that I'm going to go on living, but that I'll be committed to life, to making things come out right." *(This is encouraging. Now he's saying he's committed to "making things come out right," rather than, "It's not been getting done." He's beginning to sound as if he's taking charge of things.)*

Mary: "What does that mean to you—making things come out right?"

Tim: "Uh—making things happy—uh—doing things for my own—uh—for my own happiness. Then I'd have 60 happy years." *(This is another step toward a redecision.)*

Bob: "You said 'for my own happiness,' and shook your head 'no'. What's the other side of it?" *(Apparently, part of him is not in agreement. I want him to be in touch with that side, too, to resolve this conflict completely.)*

Tim: "The other side is, I'll live and then I'll die."

Mary: "So if you decide to live you'll have 60 happy years."

Tim: "Yeah—that doesn't sound so bad now, but, uh, I have a way of interpreting things very strongly. I listen—just listen—take sounds as if they were coming out of the tape recorder, take all sights as if they were on a movie screen, and all smells as if God was blowing smells in my nose, and mixing them all together and coming out with, uh, a . . . [*looks at Bob*] You're not interested in hearing God, are you?" *(Bob shakes head.)*

Mary: "I'm not, particularly because I'm still back with the thing you said before that—about the 60 happy years—and I don't want to be construed as promising any-body full happiness. What I'm interested in is a decision that you're going to live, period. Do you see what I mean? You can get hung up if every day has to be happy."

Tim: "Yeah, well I think I can make them pretty darn happy. I think I can—at the conclusion of each day—say I'm glad this day happened—no, that I made this day happen."

Mary: "Yeah, it's important that you separate these two—that your life doesn't depend upon each day's eval-uation—but that you decide to live no matter what."

Tim: "Yeah."

Bob: "I like what you just did, Tim, when you went back and said, 'No, I made this day happen.' You heard yourself use the 'this day happened' and you turned it around."

Tim: "Yeah, but I don't know that I cured it—by just doing it. I'm aware of that; I'm aware of a lot of things that, uh, blow my mind; there are a lot of things I'm not aware of. I haven't laughed in a long time. I'm, I'm get-ting anesthetized. I'm bored—nothing seems funny any-more. I don't say anything that's funny."

Another participant: "Remember that laugh you had when you first came?"

Tim: "I don't like that laugh; that's like blowing off steam. That laugh is all right; I'd rather laugh that laugh than no laugh, but I would much rather just laugh; and I don't know what's holding me back [*painfully*]. I don't know what's making me feel sad, making my face sad." (*Here he made a sad face, and paused.*)

Mary: "Will you go on? Put some words to that sadness you're feeling."

Tim: "Well, I seem to feel sadder when I start talking about all the things I've lost."

Mary: "All the things you've lost? What have you lost?"

Tim: "I've lost my laugh, my ability to laugh, and, uh, I've lost a relationship with a girl that started that was quite promising. I . . . well I felt like I was in control of that—the whole thing—and then I lost control. It went overboard, or else I controlled it to go overboard—either way I lost—that I lost spontaneity."

Mary: "So some of your goals for the future are to laugh more, to allow yourself to be more spontaneous, and to have a relationship with a girl or girls—[*Tim nods*] and I hear basically this, that the decision that's needed is that you're going to live—not if you're happy, or if you're spontaneous, or if you have a girl friend, but that you are going to live."

Tim: "Yeah, that's about it. I don't understand why I'm here—who made me, why this world is here, how I got here, I don't understand. I feel that there is, uh, a loving spirit around me, but that spirit is calling me to be with it, through death—through deciding to die—and I won't do it."

Mary: "It sounds right now as if at a point where you decide to act, to live, all of a sudden you trip back into some philosophizing—almost as if to take away your current action, ability to move—because you don't know how come the world is here, or how come a couple of cells join together and add up to a human being. Neither do I—but you're going off into that at a point where you're talking about committing yourself to living."

Tim: "Yeah—the thing is I want to believe that I have a pipeline to God, and I want to believe that all of you people in this room have a . . ." (*Here he went into a long diatribe about God, most of which was psychotic.*)

Mary: "See how you get yourself off your stated desire that you decide to live? By going off on a back street of depression—I don't understand that."

Tim: "I want to live—that's my computer—thinking from one part of me." (*Long, long silence; and then he frowned.*)

Bob: "What's the frown?"

Tim: "I'm nowhere again—anything I say from here on will have no meaning. It's just something I'm saying, something in my head."

Bob: "Well, you said, 'I want to live,' and you had some feelings about that, and then you frowned, and then you said that doesn't mean anything—and then you're back to what Mary was saying. At any given moment you can quickly run to something to feel bad about. Like how did I get here, or what's the world all about, or everybody is killing everybody, or something else. This ties in considerably with what we said the very first day—how I saw you doing things that ended up in your feeling bad. So that you can do something with someone else and end up feeling bad, or if that's not available, you can say 'Oh, I can feel bad about . . .'—and then pick out something to feel bad about."

Tim: "Yeah [*smiling*], I can always find something to feel bad about."

Bob: "And then you can add up enough bad things to feel even worse about. If you search hard enough, they're not too hard to find, and then you can say, 'Yeah, I can kill myself—to heck with it—it's not worth it'—and what Mary was suggesting was that you stay at this moment in feeling good about a decision you have made, rather than running off to something to feel bad about. So what I heard you say was, 'I want to decide to live'—and right at this moment, what is keeping you from saying 'I am going to live'?"

(*Long pause.*)

Tim: "I don't feel capable of receiving love [*long pause*]. It's from a human being that's not worthy of a soul—"

Mary: "I've got a hunch that you're supposed to feel bad about deciding to live," (*This is a theoretical position that Mary took—the injunction says, "Don't be," which means, "If you die I'll love you;" so, of course, if he decides to live, his little Child will not get any love, and therefore he can't feel good, an impossible situation if he stays with the injunction.*)

Tim: "Yeah."

Mary: "How come? Will you get with that?" (We ask, "will you," not "can you.")

Tim: "I can tell you my head trip on that—I'm backing away from certainty to death—I'm scared of killing myself—that's why—I'm guilty of being afraid.

"But I don't know if that's the right reason—I sure hope—[*voice drops*] it isn't."

Mary: "If you were really feeling healthy right now—really feeling good, and wow, you're going to live out the rest of your life, and know where you're going, and all that stuff; if all of a sudden you dropped the depression, dropped the philosophical side trips, and said 'Hey, wow, I'm really here. I've really made it;' will you go there in your imagination right now?"

Tim: "Yeah."

Mary: "In your imagination you say, 'Wow, I've really made it—I know where I am, I'm going to live out my life.' What's scary about that?"

Tim: "I'd have a hell of an inflated ego to believe I'm a super power, that I could control people."

Mary: "And who would you want to control—can you name somebody?"

Tim: "Well, my mother, my family, my girl friend."

Mary: "Will you see your mother in front of you now, and you say, 'Wow, I'm really there . . .'"

Tim: "Yeah"

Mary: "OK, will you tell her how you are going to control her—from your really-there position?"

Tim: "Well [*moves in his chair*]—it's not so much I wanted to control you, as I just won't buy crap from you—won't buy any crap from you—and not only that, I can see through the crap you are handing me and I can give you what you want, what you need, and what I want to give you, which is my love . . ." (*The next few words were said in a very low voice.*)

Mary: "From your really-there position—can you visualize yourself walking out the front door, and saying 'Good-bye, I'm really there, and I'm living a life for me now. And I'll see you at Christmas and Easter and when I'm in town?"

Tim: "'Good-bye'—that's a hard one to envision, that's the hardest one. 'Well, I'll be on my way—on my happy merry way—I'm leaving you to carry our load. [*Mumbles*]—You may have a mess, but I'm through with you now all right.'"

Bob: "OK, so then you leave, saying 'Good-bye, I'll see you at Christmas, and Easter, and times like that'—and what do you fantasy yourself doing between now and five years from now? I run into you in five years from now, when you stop by on your motorcycle, and I say, 'Hello. And what have you been doing, Tim?'"?

Tim: "I could be up to 80—my story . . ."

Bob: "Will you make up a story?"

Tim: "I would have found my way into a way of life."

(*He starts out very sadly, and I can see that the chances are very good he's about to go off on another sorry, philosophical, irrational, word salad. At this point, I want to hear from his creative side, from the happy, spontaneous side I knew he has, and for him to get in touch with that. He has been in this depressed jazz long enough. The idea of this exercise is to let him taste the other side—so):*

Bob: "Tim, will you go in a time machine with me? I've got a big machine here [*I drag up two chairs.*]—invisible walls, and it's a time machine. Will you get inside the time machine? [*Tim looks in.*] And we go bzzzzzzzzz, and it's 1975—OK—and here's the chair inside the machine. [*He gets in.*] We go bzzzzzzzz. It's now July 7, 1975 and I say, 'Wow! Hi, Tim, how are you?'"

(Tim and I went on a fantasy in which he imagined being successful in 1975, with great enthusiasm, and again in 1980, with great enthusiasm. We went for a ride in his newly invented steam car, for instance, and his level of excitement got higher as he fantasied events. Without the fantasy trip, I don't believe that he would have gotten in touch with his own power at this time, and would not have reached the decision he ultimately reached.

At the end of the fantasy trip, we came back to the present. I asked him if he felt good about the things he had invented. He said yes, and then we had the following dialogue.)

Bob: "So the way you got to do all these things was to look for ways to feel good?"

Tim: "Yeah."

Bob: "OK, let's go back to 1970. Will you decide to live so that you can start doing those things?"

(This was a mistake, and slowed down the process. He was in this bind because of his father's demands that he succeed, among other things, and at this point I made what I thought was a reasonable request in view of the fantasy, but which he felt was a parental demand "to do things.")

Tim: (*After a long pause, sadly*): "Yes, I decide to live; I decide not to kill myself. I decide not to go to sleep forever."

Bob: "You mean that?"

Tim: "Not all the way. I think I would be crying if I did. It's like if I decide that, I won't be able to receive love."

Bob: "I can hear what you say, and I don't believe that you won't be able to receive love."

Tim: "You don't believe it?"

Bob: "I believe that at this moment you believe it, but I don't."

Tim: "Yeah, I think you're right."

Bob: "Will you allow yourself to open up to receive love—from me?"

Tim: "Yes [*pause*]—I like the idea very much."

Bob: "So if I love you as another human being, that's OK with you?" (*I deliberately said that I could love him as a human being, not as an achiever, to get out of the bind I set up by the work demand I made previously.*)

Tim: "Yes, but it makes me feel like someone is clutching my heart."

Bob: "I have no expectations for you—and what you do with the fact that I love you as another human being . . ."

Tim: "I just can't believe that—I just look for evidence and it's not good enough."

Bob: "Do you hear me? I have no expectations for what you do—I love you as a human being."

Tim: "Yeah, I can see what you're saying more clearly. I think I have felt that, too—I know I have."

Bob: "So, how about the decision?"

(*He starts to cry. I wait for a while and then say:*)

Bob: "I think I know—and you and I can find out—a lot of reasons why you've felt the way you've felt in the past. I'm not sure it's that important to find out why, but I think we can if we look for them. I think we can find them a lot more easily, if they're important, or maybe even drop the question if it's not important, if you first decide, 'By God, no matter what happens, I am going to live. I'm not going to kill myself, accidentally or on purpose—ever.'"

Tim: "By God, I'm not going to kill myself, no matter if things get pretty tough." *(There is a two- or three-minute pause here, while he cries, Mary and I cry, and 30 other people in the room cry.)*

Mary: "I'm so very fond of you, Tim, without expectations, and with a great deal of willingness for you to say good-bye as soon as you're ready."

Tim: "I just don't know when to be sure. What are the conditions for being sure? I know I felt sure about some things. I know I can do some things, because I can feel myself behind them . . . I know I can get something done when I start it—[*mumble*]."

Bob: "That's the key. You don't know right now how you're going to make the decision come true, and that's not as important as making the decision. You—as I, and other people have—will find the way."

Tim: "It seems like my voice is going to betray me, if I promise . . ."

Bob: "I'm not asking you for a promise. This is a decision for you, not a promise to me. I'm here asking you to look at it, and decide it, for you. Not for mother, not for father, not for anybody else—not for Mary, not for Virginia, but for Tim, for you."

Tim: "Yeah"

Bob: "Then you can say good-bye to mother, good-bye to father, good-bye to Mary, good-bye to me, in all kinds of ways; then get on your motorcycle and ride over the mountains. The decision about living is for you."

Tim: "Sometimes life isn't really worth it."

Bob: "I know."

Tim: "This last week has not been."

Bob: "I know that sometimes life looks like it isn't worth it."

Tim: "Then why live, if it's not worth it, even for one day?"

Bob: "Why die if it is?"

Tim: "I know the last week hasn't been worth it."

Bob: "Are you blocking out the next ten thousand days? Because of your experience in the last week?"

Tim: "Yeah."

Bob: "I think that you've been living under the early decision you made a long time ago not to live. You've been struggling with it a long time. And as long as you're in that struggle, whether or not to, then you'll always find black clouds."

Tim: "Yeah, that's true."

Bob: "Yeah, I know, I've heard you."

Tim: *(With a warm chuckle.)* "I can always find white clouds too."

Bob: "That's right, and I've heard that, too. I don't think you know what it feels like to say 'Hey, I'm going to live, I'm going to live. That's a decision I can make.' I don't think you know what it feels like to make that decision. And you're never going to find out what it's like, until you make it."

Tim: *(Crying.)* "It's for me, the decision is for me! It's really for me. It's for me, it's for me. Not for you, not for [*this is said very softly*] anyone. It's for me, to commit myself to life, to commit myself to something that's going to end in 70 years."

Bob: "Or 80, or 90, or 100."

Tim: "Yeah [*long sigh, sniffle*]—uh—I suppose it doesn't matter how long you, and everyone else in this room waits for me. [*Pause*] I'm not going to kill myself."

His Father (*who was there*): "You really mean that?"

Mary: "At this moment will you be your mother, and say what you want to hear? Will you sit in this chair, and tell Tim, Mother."

Tim (*as Mother*): "Gee, that's too bad. I'd rather have you for my own than have you free."

Mary: "Will you be Tim and answer that?"

Tim: "That's too bad." (*There was a resolution of the old Oedipal situation at this point, and he laughed, then grinned happily.*)

Bob: "You did a good job on that."

Tim: "Yeah, I'm not going to kill myself. That's the way it is. I'm not going to kill myself."

Mary: "Will you tell your father?"

Tim: "All I see of him is a shell."

Mary: "Will you tell him anyway?"

Tim: "Tell a shell?"

Mary: "Yeah."

Tim: "Dad, I'm not going to kill myself. It's ridiculous. I'm not going to kill myself."

Tim (*as Dad*): "You aren't?" [*In an entirely different voice.*] Well, I'd rather have you kill yourself than live a life like Uncle Tom."

(*Apparently, Uncle Tom was the family ne'er-do-well— and so now we see what the injunctions were: Mother said, "Don't grow up, stay my little boy." And father said from his Parent, "Succeed," and from his Child, "Kill yourself"— better dead than no good.*)

Mary: "Will you respond to that?"

Tim: (*as self*): "That's tough. [*Firmly.*] I'm not going to kill myself. I'm sorry. [*Then his face lit up with a great smile.*] I'm not sorry, Dad."

(Everyone in the room laughed with relief, enjoying this crucial last remark. And it really was crucial—the first automatic "I'm sorry" was a cop-out, which he immediately heard and retracted.)

(Tim then started to sob, and after a minute or two I said:)

Bob: "Like you said, when you mean it you'll cry. I want to stop now."

(Everyone then talked to Tim, and hugged him, stroking him for an important change in his life, instead of hugging and stroking him for the old rackets.)

Follow-up. Tim then went east for several months, and got a job on the east coast. Some time later, his sister visited him and offered to supply him with grass, LSD, or any other drug he might want. Tim's response to her offer was, *"I've decided not to kill myself—and that's a way to kill myself—I'm not buying!"*

6   *The Two Parents*   —M.M.G.

Everyone has two separate and distinct Parental ego states. In most cases they are the mother and the father the person experienced in childhood. The first, the "influencing" Parent, speaks to the person's Child. The second, the "active" Parent, deals with the outside world and talks to the P, A or C of others.

Influencing Parent:

The influencing Parent speaks only to the Child, although others may overhear the messages, as when a patient says, "You shouldn't tell your troubles in public," and *you* clearly refers to the patient's Child. Often the therapist does not hear the Parent, but infers a Parent-Child transaction from the Child response: blushing, stammering, evading, sobbing, whining, etc. This Parent tells the Child how to feel and how to behave. Also, this Parent gives negative and positive strokes to the Child.

Only the person's Child feels the presence of this Parent. Fortunately, however, one's Child and Adult can readily identify this Parent to the therapist. For example, when a therapist, noting a patient blush, asks, "What was going on inside you just then?" the patient can, if he chooses, tell the therapist exactly what the influencing

First appeared in somewhat different form in *Transactional Analysis Bulletin*, 1968, 7(26), 37-38.

Parent was saying. When a therapist says, "That is your Parent," a patient will assume the therapist is talking about the influencing Parent; therapeutic errors can result from failing to distinguish between the two Parents.

The influencing Parent is the mother, or whoever functioned as mother, the indispensable, nurturing person in the child's life. Many individuals incorrectly identify the influencing Parent as the father, particularly when the messages are in response to scholastic or business success or failure. ("Good boy to be elected president of Kiwanis," or, "You're a failure for not selling that man a life insurance policy.") Actually, although the father may have given direct messages about school and work, the prototype of these messages came from the mother at a much earlier age, and centered around creeping, self-feeding bowel training, etc. It is the mother, the influencing Parent, who continues to give messages about success and failure. Although she does not talk to the outside world, she tells the Child how to feel about strangers, and places restrictions on his behavior toward them.

Active Parent:

The active Parent transacts with the P, A or C of others, but does not talk directly with the Child ego state of the person. This Parent tells people what to do, what to think, how to behave. He has opinions on baseball strategy, divorce, sex, and Vietnam. (An "enlightened" active Parent may argue for masturbation as the key to mental health, while the influencing Parent continues to tell the Child to feel guilty about masturbatory fantasies.) In a treatment group, other patients and the therapist know this Parent well, as they feel his impact. Often, however, the patient seems not to know the Parent at all, saying, "That's not my Parent. It must be my Adult." The same patient rarely makes this error in identifying the influencing Parent.

This active Parent is the actual parent whom the child saw as family spokesman in dealings with the outside world. I believe this Parent is most often the father. However, when the child has limited or no contact with the father, when the mother is seen as dominating, this Parent may also be the mother, as the child watched her at a later stage in his childhood development. I believe this ego state develops later than that of the influencing Parent. (In some families the older brother may take the place of the father, and may be the active Parent.) Examples:

1. A woman continued to state, in opposition to the therapist and other patients, that her Parental messages were Adult messages. Her *active* Parent functioned as a benign teacher, delivering calm, reasonable, well-documented opinions on what the other patients should do. This parent is her father, a professor. The patient readily recognized her *influencing* Parent, *mother*, who told her Child that she was really weak and helpless.

2. A career noncommissioned officer bellowed at his children, "Get that lawn mowed now!" They usually obeyed, but casually, as they recognized this Parent as bombastic but benign. He did not recognize this (the active) Parent. After several months of treatment, in fact, he would say to group members, "I want you to listen to this! This is Adult information." The Parent he recognized was the influencing one, who exaggerated his small flaws into major failures and gave him messages that he would never be promoted. This was his bitter, carping mother, he said.

3. A college student delivered long, pointless sermons, to the great annoyance of fellow students and teachers. In treatment, when asked the point of a sermon, he did

not know. His Adult and Child tuned out that active Parent, just as he tuned out his real father. He listened to his influencing Parent, his mother, who gave him lots of internal strokes but restricted his spontaneity, especially in sexual matters.

(Editorial note by Eric Berne: "This article is an excellent clarification which solves one of the major problems in structural analysis. It should be carefully read by all practitioners and teachers of TA.")

7 *No Magic at Mt. Madonna: Redecisions in Marathon Therapy*
—R.L.G.

In this chapter, I will present the history of marathons as we have done them; I will define a marathon as I see the definition; I will present the therapeutic indications for doing marathons; I will present the scene and the format, as I think they ought to be done; I will review what the factors are that seem to establish an environment conducive to change; I will briefly touch on some of the results of our work.

Early Marathon Experiences

My first marathon, over Labor Day weekend in 1963 at Big Sur, California, was designed at the request of four couples in an ongoing group. These eight people said in effect, "Hey, we are doing great, but sometimes we just seem to get warmed up on something when the hour and a half is over—and by the time we get back the following

First appeared in somewhat different form in *Transactional Analysis after Eric Berne,* Graham Barnes (Ed.), New York: Harper and Row, 1977. Used by permission.

week, the desire, or the intensity, or the energy is gone. How about having a longer group once in awhile?" The request seemed reasonable to me, and I arranged for a large house in Big Sur for the weekend. We started Friday night, worked until very late, started Saturday morning, worked until after midnight, then all day Sunday, and part of Monday. Only three couples came. I was greatly impressed, as were the patients, that we did seem to get farther; we stayed with impasses until we were through them, and a great deal of wonderful, warm intimacy was developed which these people never lost in the years afterwards.

My next marathon-like experience was with Virginia Satir, also at Big Sur. There were five families and one divorcee. I believe this was also Virginia's first prolonged experience as a group leader. We started Sunday night, worked until Friday noon, with time out, of course, to eat and sleep.

The results, we thought, were interesting. The divorcee was married a few months later. One couple is still together and has not been in therapy since the week-long experience. One family consisted of a mother and daughter, who had been clashing for 18 years—ever since the daughter was adopted (the father did not come to the experience); at the end of the week, the mother and daughter had finished most of their disagreements, made some decisions to change their way of dealing with one another, and they have done well since then. Incidentally, most of the problems between mother and father also were ironed out, even though father was not there.

For several months thereafter I did an occasional weekend marathon, but did not really want to get involved— it was tough doing them by myself and at that time I had no associate to work with. Later on, I heard George Bach talk about his sleepless marathons. I had by then associated with a psychologist; over a period of months he and I did several marathons without sleep. These, in my opinion, were horrors. We started Friday evening at 6:00, stayed together working, eating, swimming until 10:00 Saturday night; slept a little, then finished Sunday at 4:00 P.M. I was not impressed with results being any better than with reasonable sleep; I *was* impressed with the fact that I lost two or three days' work each week after such a marathon, while I tried to recover from the fatigue. I felt, and the patients did also, that the lack of sleep seriously interfered with their ability to do good intellectual work; and that they probably had more emotional crises but were unable to put them together as well. After a few months I decided that sleepless marathons were for those (in the words of Price Cobbs) who are either under 40 or think they are—and, since I am neither under 40 nor think I am, I stopped the sleepless weekends.

Since that time, I have done a marathon almost every fourth weekend; occasionally I have done three a month, always (except once) with a cotherapist. We sleep six to nine hours Friday and Saturday nights. This does not meet the definition of a marathon as George Bach describes it, but in my opinion an intensive therapeutic experience that lasts through two nights, with approximately 18 hours of time spent in therapy, is a marathon. (People are on the grounds for 56 hours, 18 of which are spent in therapy.)

Criteria for Placing Patients in Marathons

For the patient already in treatment with us, there are several indications we use for placing him in a marathon. However, we do not suggest to him that he go into a marathon; rather, we allow him or her to volunteer first. At one time we did urge such patients to attend marathons, but we realized that we were letting our own enthusiasm get in the way of what might be better judgment if we waited for the patient to volunteer. He usually does so at a point that Fritz Perls called the impasse—where he is making no gains in therapy, has not reached his most recent contract goal, and thinks he needs a therapeutic experience more intense than that afforded in ongoing groups. Sometimes other patients urge that he get into a marathon, and we do nothing to bridle their enthusiasm. The second indication for the ongoing patient is often his inability to get close to people; he then wants the experience primarily for the opportunity to develop more intimate feelings for other people. Another indication is the impasse arrived at by couples or families, at which point they feel that a weekend together may enable them to discontinue their marital games. Also an important indication is the desire of a patient who has been moving rapidly to get into a marathon in order to finish his contract and discontinue therapy.

For the new patient, or new couple, or new family, we do not wait for them to volunteer. Most patients, in the initial interview, are told about the marathons and are asked to plan for one in the near future after they start therapy. It has been our opinion that many patients, if they get into a marathon early in treatment, reach their contract goals much more quickly, and can get out of therapy with the crisis in question solved. We recognize in this, then, the statement that most of our therapy today is crisis-intervention therapy; not only do we have no objection to this, we heartily endorse this type of psychotherapeutic experience. The gate to our institute opens both ways.

A third category of indications for a marathon concerns training (see section below on "The Therapist-Patient"). The professional who is in training is expected to be in a marathon and to make a therapeutic contract for himself.

Contraindications for Marathons

I will not treat in a marathon an alcoholic who is actively drinking or one who has just recently stopped drinking. This decision came after one patient on two occasions had a *grand mal* seizure following three or four days of drying out prior to the marathon. I will not treat an acute psychotic in a marathon, nor will I treat a seriously depressed and acutely suicidal patient who has not reached a decision not to kill himself.

This does not mean that we do not treat the chronic depressive in a marathon; but the acute, severely depressed patient who is still ruminating about suicide is too difficult to handle in a marathon and takes too much time from the other patients. We want the hard drug user off drugs for a while before we do a marathon with him. There may be some other contraindications but these seem to cover most. We have made no attempts to eliminate patients because of physical disabilities. If another physician did not want his patient to go to a marathon because of cardiac disease or other contraindications, I would honor his decision.

For the above reasons we will take no patient in a marathon unless he is our own patient, or has been referred to us by a professional who, preferably, has been to one of our marathons. We do take professionals into marathons without referral. We have had professionals who fell into the contraindicated categories, and we have dealt with each of them on an individual basis. I believe that the reason we have had almost no untoward reactions in 14 years is because we take seriously our responsibility for the patient. Some workshop and marathon leaders have written that the professional (or patient) arrives under his own steam, is responsible for doing so, and is responsible for himself. I do not feel this position is medically responsible and would not allow a distraught participant to leave without some definite plans for his immediate care.

The Marathon Format

We hold most of our intensive experiences on a 30-acre farm in the mountains outside Watsonville, California. The house is big enough to sleep 20 participants comfortably, although we seldom have more than 14. We have a good kitchen, a good cook, and good food. Everyone sleeps in beds, although at one time when we first did marathons everyone slept on the floor in the living room on sleeping bags and air mattresses. We have a swimming pool, because we believe that swimming, exercise, and some play are important to encourage the participants to have fun together as well as to work. (We have treated many patients with phobias about water by teaching them to swim while we were concurrently working on the source of the phobic feelings in the therapeutic environment. See below.)

We start the weekend at 9:00 A.M. Friday with a presentation on transactional analysis theory. Patients seem to be able to put things together much better with the orderly presentation of the theoretical material, and this emphasizes the view of TA therapists that they share with the patient their theoretical and practical ideas, so that the patient is not in the dark regarding the therapeutic process.

We break at noon for lunch; unlike Bach, we allow the participants to eat wherever they like—with each other in the dining room, or around the pool, or by themselves. We think that patients should have the opportunity to withdraw for a while if they wish. Formerly we picked up the theoretical material again at 1:00 P.M., but now we start therapy at 1:30 and continue working until about 5:00. In the past, we had the participants lead small groups under our supervision to begin to get some experience in the use of the theory; we have discontinued this, because we found it somewhat disjointed and often not productive.

At the start of the marathon, we announce the following rules:

1. The use of alcohol, drugs, and marijuana is prohibited, and anyone having any illegal drugs on the premises is asked to take them across the road and bury them. Anyone taking a prescription is asked to notify me of the nature of the drug.
2. No physical violence will be permitted, and no breaking of furniture is allowed unless it is first paid for.
3. No one is permitted to leave the property, but participants can withdraw at any time if they wish; there are 30 acres and 20 rooms to withdraw to.
4. No sexual intercourse is allowed except between married couples or partners who have been living together.

5. Any food or nonalcoholic beverage in the house may be eaten or drunk at any time.

If anyone questions the reasons for the rules, we explain them. We want people to be in the best possible shape to work—and neither alcohol nor drugs are conducive to good work. I do not want pot on the place because it is against the law. Physical violence is not therapeutic. Furniture costs money. Sex between participants not married to one another or previously living together often is gamy ("Rapo") and ends in difficulty.

At 1:30 we start the formal work of the marathon. During the afternoon on Friday we obtain contracts for the weekend from each participant—patient and professional alike. A therapeutic contract is one of the most important tools of the group therapist. If the therapist and the patient know where the patient wants to go, then they can tell when they get there, and the therapist will usually be able to identify the sideroads down which the patient goes as not in the interest of the contract.

Getting the contracts usually takes all of Friday afternoon. This does not mean that no therapeutic work is done; frequently, at the time a contract is made, some of the most important work in fulfilling it is done. We use several therapeutic tools. We are basically transactional analysts, and use TA as our primary theoretical position; we also use a great deal of gestalt therapy and our own brand of psychodrama. Our marathons are designed for the patient to contract to have new experiences for himself. We are discriminating in the use of nonverbal and verbal techniques; the particular technique has to fit the needs of a particular patient at a particular time. In other words, we don't suddenly say to the patients, "Now let's everyone do Technique 23A," or use gimmicks, or sensory awareness exercises, or other such ploys unless they fit in the therapeutic scheme for a particular problem.

These marathons are intensive therapeutic experiences and not sensory awareness weekends.

We formerly stopped work at about midnight, but have since found it wiser to quit at 9:00 P.M. Saturday morning we start at 9:00, with breakfast served at about 7:30. We usually work for about one and a half hours, then break for an encounter-group session made up of three or four small groups. This is to allow the less assertive patients to have more of a chance to transact and interact, and often some good experiences come out of the encounters. When we meet again, a half-hour later, we ask for unfinished business from the encounters so that if there are any loose ends we can work them out. We break at noon for lunch and a swim, and at 5:00 for dinner and a swim; then work until everyone is satisfied with where they are at the moment. Usually we quit at about 8:30 or 9:00 P.M., and then we have a dry party, with music, dancing, and games if the group wishes. Mary, my wife, and I usually take part in the party for a half-hour or so, then leave and allow the participants some time together without us, and us some time without them. We have heard that they usually have more fun after we have left.

Sunday morning we start again at 9:00 and work until noon. Sunday is usually the time for dream work, and this is one of the many therapeutic reasons why I prefer doing marathons in which patients can sleep. Frequently some very important dream work is done, and it crystallizes the weekend experience for a number of patients. We prefer active, in-the-present work, in which the patient relives the dream, takes the various parts in it, and then retells it the way he wants it, perhaps by changing the ending.

Beginning at 11:00 A.M. Sunday we wind up with a discussion of redecisions, in which the participants review individually what they are going to do differently in the future. This frequently is a most important part of the marathon. For instance, when the depressed patient states that he is not going to kill himself, and that he is going to enjoy himself in the future, it is often the start of a new life, in which he checks out what he does day in and day out against that decision.

Following the redecisions, the patients are allowed time to say good-bye to each other. Many patients have been working all weekend on saying good-bye to old figures in their lives and to old feelings. The experience of saying good-bye to the group members, and to their group transferences, is often extremely important.

Effectiveness of Marathon Group Treatment

If we assume that this method of treatment is effective, and perhaps more effective than other methods of individual or group psychotherapy, we need to postulate what the effective factors are. In our opinion, there are at least three reasons for what we believe to be more effective therapy in many cases. The first is time itself; the patients are exposed to interventions, self-discovery, and redecisions over a prolonged period, where they are not as likely to use their common defenses, and where they cannot so easily withdraw or delay until the hour is up. Although they may withdraw and although we always give participants a chance to stop at any point they wish, the recognition that others have made changes without disaster, that others have broken through some old patterns without the walls falling down, encourages each one to do more for himself. This last point brings home the second issue: the patient is stimulated by the intensity of peer pressure and peer encouragement over a prolonged period, and rewarded by the recognition that he or she gets for doing a particularly important piece of work. Thirdly, the degree of intimacy that builds up in 56 hours makes it easier for patients to feel safer in working through impasses. Thus it would seem that the prolonged time involved, the difficulty in withdrawing, the increased stroking, and the awareness that others are making immediate changes all add up to increased opportunity for change for each patient.

The results of marathon group treatment are difficult to evaluate scientifically, but we do have two specific pieces of research that are supportive. One is the work done by Lieberman, Yalom, and Miles (1973) reported in the book *Encounter Groups: First Facts.* The other is the dissertation, by John McNeel (1975) for his PhD, on one of our weekend marathons. We have enough feedback from both patients and professionals to know that our participants very often make changes in their behavior as well as their feelings after attending marathons. We have feedback from organizations such as the O. H. Close School, an agency in the California Youth Authority, that their staff members, after attending a training marathon, seem to work better together, to stop their institutional games faster, and to be generally happier (McCormick, 1973). Many of our patients tell us that they accomplished more in a marathon than they had in several months of group treatment. All these reports are somewhat intangible, and I cannot and will not claim that we have proof positive that marathons are better than weekly group sessions, or individual sessions, or prolonged psychoanalysis. It is even difficult to evaluate whether the marathon is the primary agent, or whether it is our technique, our enthusiasm, and our abilities that set the stage for the possibility of change. McNeel's work cites four major areas which the clients in his research of one of our marathons stated were helpful:

1. the environment—physical and personal
2. positive recognition
3. the therapists' modeling behavior
4. the techniques—experiential and cognitive

This brings me to Eric Berne, who was more interested in working with patients to change (he called it "cure") than in finding out why they behaved as they did. He said, "Cure the patient, then analyze."

I first met Eric in Carmel before my psychiatric residency, played poker a few times with him, but had no professional contact. I had intended to finish my analysis with him, since my analyst in Baltimore had died. I phoned him in January of 1962, on my way to Roseburg, Oregon, where I had been assigned for two years as part of my Veterans Administration contract, and made an appointment to see him the following Saturday. During that week, Carl Bonner asked me if I had read a book on transactional analysis by ". . .a fella named Eric Berne" (1961). "Wow," said I, "I'm going to see him Saturday. Let me borrow it." So I read it, and turned on. When I saw Eric, I told him right off that I wanted both to finish my analysis and learn TA from him. "Well," he intoned, "that would be kinda sticky." I can still hear him. I was in supervision with him almost every Saturday for two years—driving down from Roseburg to Carmel (600 miles) on Friday and back on Sunday for the first year and a half. In June, 1963, I was transferred to Palo Alto, so I only had to drive 60 miles to Carmel, and I was able to attend most of the Tuesday night seminars in San Francisco. Sometime during those two years I started the Carmel Institute for Transactional Analysis to train some of the professionals in Carmel as well as the nonprofessionals who were interested in community mental health.

Later Mary and I expanded the training offered by the institute to include intensive month-long workshops, and for the past several years professionals from all over the world have trained with us and our associates. We also changed our institute's name to the Western Institute for Group and Family Therapy, and moved to Mount Madonna, near Watsonville, California, overlooking beautiful Monterey Bay.

Rackets

From the very first moment, the trainee/patient at Mount Madonna is confronted with the awareness that he alone is in charge of his thinking, behavior, and feelings. He possesses the power. If he chooses to feel angry, or sad, or anxious, or confused, that is his choice, and he has other options. This concept is the very core of our work. Furthermore, he looks for his original power in being anxious, or angry, or sad, and for what that feeling originally got him. The feelings, appropriately called *rackets* by Berne, were developed in order for him to manipulate his parents into giving him what he wanted, and he is still doing something, and feeling something, so as to manipulate other people. Unfortunately, most of the rackety feelings he may still have are also designed to change the past, as well as the present. Since this cannot be done, the bad feelings are maintained so as to perpetuate a magical belief, and are without any good return.

Injunctions/Decisions

The patients are confronted with the *decisions* they made early in response to their injunctions, and which they are still maintaining. These were *their* decisions in response to the behavior and feelings of their parents; the injunctions were not stuck into their heads like electrodes, but they responded to them in order to survive both psychologically and physiologically. They had the power to make the decisions, and they have the power to make new ones now, in this time, in this place, if they do not like what they are doing, what they are feeling, what they are thinking now. Their rackets, their games, their pastimes, all support the original decision, and they have the power to change it. Leading them to change it is the essence of what we do.

Game Confrontation

Patients have the power to do whatever within reason they want to do. We create an environment in which the patients may recapture their autonomy. We supply surroundings that are most conducive to that purpose; the patient has little to do each day but work on himself and play. His food is supplied, everyone around him is giving him positive strokes, no one is parenting him, no one is bossing him. At the same time, whenever he gives an indication that he is staying in a bad place, or feeling bad inappropriately, he is confronted by staff and by other patients. If he laughs while talking about feeling bad while at the table, I will say, "That's not funny," or "I'm not laughing." If he arrives before the stated time of 7:00 P.M. and finds the gate locked (as it is), and if he feels anger, or chagrin, or whatever, we immediately ask him how come he set himself up to feel bad when he knew the gate would be locked. If he calls to say that he would like to come early, and gets angry when we say no, or feels we have rejected him, we immediately confront him with his game of "Kick Me."

The confrontation of the game is done very simply. The patient is asked what he is feeling. In the case of coming early and finding the gate locked, he usually is angry that we will not let him in until 7:00. We ask him if he wants to know how he did it—how he set himself up to get angry. Usually he is willing to find out. Then we draw the game out by using the Goulding-Kupfer sequence representation of the game.

His ostensibly straight message (Adult to Adult) is, "Please open the gate." His secret message (Child to Parent) is, "Say no so that I can be angry." We of course say no, because we have already written everyone a letter with directions and the explicit statement not to come early because the gate will be locked; his Child must know that, even though he is keeping it out of the awareness of his Adult. He then takes his payoff, which in this case is anger, and says inside his head, or out loud, "No one ever gives me what I want," and, "Everyone in the world is a son of a bitch." Of course, the entire process is out of his Adult's awareness—the process that he sets up so that he can maintain his anger at a world that refuses to give him what he wants.

We may then ask him what he will do if he continues to make himself angry in this manner for the next five years. What will be his predictable behavior? He may say that he will kill someone in anger and go to jail. He may say that he gets so disgusted that he will kill himself in anger. He may say that people get tired of his anger, and he will end up alone. Whatever he says, it is his *script payoff*, and we ask him if this is what he really wants out of his life. If it is not, we ask him whether he is willing to stop playing the game and stop taking the payoff. We usually get an, "Of course." Then we want to know what he predicts he will do if he plays again. He'll usually say that he would angrily kick himself—thus, of course, continuing to play all by himself. We then ask him if he is willing, at the moment he recognizes he has played, to refuse the anger and instead feel good that he has recognized the game. Practice is all he needs, for if he doesn't get the payoff, his Child will stop playing after a while.

Redecision

The next piece of work is to get him into an early scene in which he gets angry, and in which he says the things he said above about himself and others, including, "I never get what I want," and, "You're a son of a bitch." Then we give him the opportunity to make a *redecision* about getting what he wants appropriately.

The Therapist-Trainee as Patient

Recognize, of course, that in our current work 90 percent or more of our "patients" are therapists. We take no nontherapists into our one-week, two-week, or four-week workshops, and no patients in our ongoing training; only a few patients make the marathons, usually because therapists have signed up for them a year in advance. However, almost everyone who comes has problems to work out. My position is that training *must* include therapy; a depressed therapist has a difficult time treating anyone, and more particularly, depressed patients; phobic therapists (and there are a lot of them) have great difficulty in treating phobics. Male "Rapo" players get involved over and over again with female hysterics. Female therapists of any age who are still little girls have very little potency and find it difficult to confront patients. Psychotic therapists give their patients many negative injunctions, which may cause the patients to get worse instead of better. Suicidal therapists often give their patients "Don't be" injunctions.

Thus, to train without treatment neglects one of the most important issues in training—the trainee. He or she has to be of sound emotional stability in order to be most effective, and therefore the very core of our training is that the therapists are patients as well as therapists. To take the magic out of therapy, they constantly change roles; that is, John may be Susan's therapist at 9:00 A.M. and Susan's patient at 10:00 A.M. At the time I am writing this, I am just completing a two-week advanced workshop and, by the time the group got to the last weekend when Mary and I were to do a marathon, most of the members of the workshop were finished with their work. Advanced therapy, conducted by good therapists in this environment, leads to very rapid resolution of all kinds of archaic impasses and to the beginnings of substantial, permanent changes. That does not mean that, after a week, a depressed therapist gives up all his depression forever; it does mean that he usually gives up all thoughts of suicide, and begins to take charge of his own sadness, and to stop playing games and fantasying in order to feel depressed. He gets in touch with his own power, and claims it.

That may sound simple, and it is, but there is no magic in it. It takes very careful work, and it takes a lot of practice. The patient has to *know* that he is in charge, and he has had years of conditioning which tell him that he is not in charge, that other people *make* him feel angry, or sad, or anxious. He reads this in books, his culture believes it, even the songs he hears say that people make other people hurt, or fall in love. "You made me love you; I didn't want to do it." Mother says, "You were a very difficult birth; you tore me up!" Or, "If it weren't for you, I wouldn't have had to marry your father!" My God, who fucked?

That is the kind of trash we were raised with, and most of the world believes it. Mother controls behavior by saying, "You make me so angry," or, "You give me a headache," or, "You make me worry so when you are not in by nine." So part of the work is in behavior—and thinking, and feeling—modification—operant conditioning. Every time someone says, "How does she make you feel?" or, "He made me feel bad," we holler, "Tilt." Every time. We constantly recondition our patients. Every time they say, "Try," as in "Yes, I'll try not to say 'makes me feel,'" I ring a huge cow bell. We teach people how to be in touch with their immediate surroundings instead of harassing themselves by thinking of what they did yesterday that was wrong, or being anxious about what they are going to do tomorrow. Most of the difficulty people have is in not staying in the here-and-now, by anticipating the future or rehashing the past. There is usually no way of feeling bad if I stay in the present, in this place, unless this is a bad place, and then I will get the hell out of it. If I cannot get out of it—as the prisoners at Marion Federal Penitentiary cannot—then I will find a way of making it a better place, as Martin Groder has done in his work with prisons.

Degrees of Impasses

Thus we keep up a constant modification of whatever behavior or thinking or feeling that is inappropriate to the present and to the idea of autonomy. We use gestalt work to facilitate people getting through impasses, and we see impasses as being of only three basic kinds: (1) between A_1 and P_2; (2) between A_1 and P_1 (which Berne called the electrode); or (3) between the Adapted Child and the Free Child. All impasses relate directly to the Little Professor (A_1) having decided something in order to get along, and now not wanting to do that anymore. Decisions cannot be made in the Adult to produce comfortable change; they must be made from the Adult of the Child (A_1). See Figure 1.

For example, in the first-degree impasse (degrees refer to type, not severity), the patient decided at one time, from his Little Professor, to listen to and obey a counter-injunction—a message from the Parent ego state of his parent—to "Work hard" or "Whatever you do, do it well or don't do it at all." All therapists probably received one or the other or both of these. No one would get to be a professional therapist if he hadn't worked hard to get through college, get through graduate or medical school, or get through clinical training in psychotherapy. At some point the therapist says to himself, "I don't want to work so hard anymore; I am going to cut down to 40 or 50 hours a week" (A_2). And so he does, and perhaps he will get away with no problems, and resolve the impasse simply. The impasse is the conflict between the introjected Parent saying, "Work hard," and the Child saying, "I don't wanna anymore." The Adult making the decision not to work hard is probably not enough; the Child feels deprived because he wasn't consulted about something that had gotten him a lot of strokes (for working hard),

Figure 1

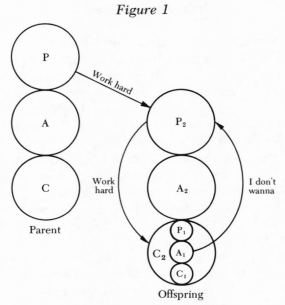

First-degree impasse (P_2–A_1)

and he rebels. The rebellion may be in the form of anxiety and restlessnes, with difficulty in structuring time; it may be in headaches, or insomnia, or a feeling of despair.

More work then needs to be done to resolve the first-degree impasse. For instance, the therapist may complain that since he decided yesterday not to work so hard, he has a headache. I may say: "Think of a scene in which your mother or father told you to work hard."

Patient: "I was seven years old and . . ."

I: "Be in the present tense."

Patient: "I am seven years old and I want a bicycle. My father says, 'You can't have a bicycle unless you do something for it.' I say, 'What?' 'Well . . .'"

I: "Move over in the chair and be your father."

Patient *(as Father)*: "If you are going to get anywhere in this world, you are going to have to work for it, and work hard."

I: "Switch."

Patient *(as self, switching)*: "I'm just a little boy, and I want a bike, and I don't want to work hard. You give me a bike for Christmas."

Patient *(as Father)*: "No, you have to work hard to get anything; bikes don't grow on trees."

Patient: "What do you want me to do?"

I: "OK, you gave in. What would you really like to tell him? *Be* there."

Patient: "You son of a bitch, I'm not always going to work hard to get what I want. All you think of is work. I'm playing more, working less from now on." *(Headache stops.)*

A day or two later, the patient may say, "OK, my headache is gone, but now I'm beginning to feel depressed. It seems like I keep hearing in my head my mother's voice saying, 'If you are not going to work hard and make me proud of you, you might as well be dead.'"

Now we are working through the injunction, "Don't exist," and the Child's response to the injunction could be, "If I'm not working hard, no one will stroke me, and I might as well go out and eat worms." The second-degree impasse relates to the Child's awareness of the "Don't be" injunction, and his uneasiness with not resolving it at this time (Figure 2). "Respond to your mother," I say.

Patient: "I remember you saying things like that."

I: "*Be* there."

Patient: "How come you don't want me unless I work hard?"

Patient *(as Mother)*: "I never wanted you. It was your father's idea; if you must be here, you're going to have to work."

Figure 2 .

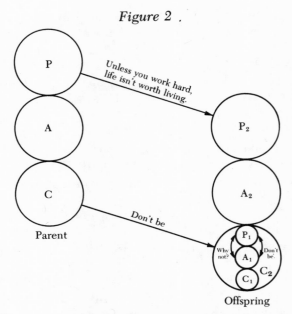

Second-degree impasse (P_1-A_1)

Patient *(as self)*: "Well, to hell with you. I'm not going to work hard, and I'm not only going to stay alive, I am going to start living, not just existing for you to be proud of. I'm going to play, and have fun, and enjoy myself and my life. Furthermore, I'm going to buy my own damn bike [*laughing*]."

It is even possible that he may return in a couple of days and say, "Well, I don't feel depressed anymore, but I sure am uncomfortable somehow. I feel worthless. As a matter of fact, I have always felt worthless unless I was doing something. I can remember helping my mother when I was only a little tiny kid, and I felt worthless then."

Now we are dealing with the third-degree impasse, the Adapted Child feeling that has "always" been there. Always worthless, always clumsy, always nervous, always stupid. (The second generation Mexican-American in California is called and feels stupid because he does not speak much English, but nobody calls the teacher stupid for not speaking Spanish. Nobody calls the other kids stupid for not speaking Spanish either.) The Adapted Child does not experience the injunction as coming from outside; rather he experiences that any comments coming from mother, or teacher, or other students were justified because he *was* stupid, or clumsy, or worthless.

In this, the third-degree impasse, the conflict is not between the Child or Parent of the parent and the Child's Little Professor; it is between the Adapted Child and the Free Child. Now, instead of an I-Thou dialogue, it is com-

Figure 3

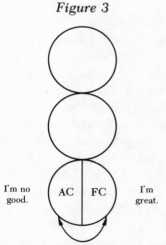

Third-degree impasse (AC–FC)

prised of two statements; one from the Free Child, one from the Adapted Child. For instance:

Adapted Child: "I have always felt worthless. I remember feeling worthless when I was a little kid, and I had to keep doing things not to feel worthless."

Free Child: "I don't know what to say from this side."

I: "Stand over here near that chair. Pretend you are just born there on the chair, and tell you why you're worthless."

Patient: "I won't do that. He's not worthless at all; he's just born, and he's cute."

I: "Sit in that chair and say that for you."

Free Child: "Hey, I'm a great little kid, and if those other guys don't appreciate me that's their problem." *(Switches).*

Adapted Child: "Yeah, I'm tired of feeling worthless. I think I'll give it up."

Free Child: "I know I'm giving it up." *(Note the use of the future tense in the Adapted position, the use of the present tense in the Free position.)*

Adapted Child: "Now I'm feeling great. I am great."

We use behavior modification, gestalt, Wolpe's (1969) desensitization, psychodrama, anything at all that will facilitate the patient getting into his Child ego state in an archaic scene, making sure that he or she is there with affect, reliving the scene, and then making a new decision. We use TA as a structure of thinking for ourselves, asking ourselves the same questions over and over again: What is the racket? What kinds of games does the patient play? What were the decisions that he made as a child? What were the injunctions and counterinjunctions? We move as rapidly as possible to get the patient to work through the impasse, and *then* we give him cognitive feedback by word of mouth and by visual imagery, using the script matrix drawings and diagrams of games (both

Karpman's [1968] triangle and the Goulding-Kupfer sequence). The moderate affective experience, the maximum cognitive feedback, the maximum caring, all in a moderately controlled environment, will bring about the best results, as long as the patient maintains his autonomy. Any attempt to discount the autonomy of the patient may end eventually in either a psychotic or neurotic symbiosis.

Treatment of Phobias

We are particularly interested in fast work. Berne said long ago that every time he started a group, he spent a few minutes before entering the room planning on how he could cure everyone that day. That is a fascinating concept, and we use it as the primary goal in our therapy. We ask ourselves what kind of a situation can we develop that will enable the patient to get to the very heart of his impasse, get through the impasse, and change today. Now, we know that he will not make a complete change today, but perhaps we can do something so that he makes a substantial, powerful redecision that will enable him to look at the world through a different pair of eyes and see himself in the world differently. The treatment of phobias is an example of this kind of work. In most cases we can facilitate a patient losing his phobia in 20 to 30 minutes. For instance, we work with many therapists who are phobic of heights, of water, and of insects. Some of the most fun we have is in facilitating them not to be phobic after one session of work.

Our basic position about phobias is that the phobic response is the result of an injunction and that, in such phobias as fear of high places or fear of drowning, the Little

Professor said at one time, in response to a "Don't be" injunction, "That's pretty scary; I had better be careful of high places [water, etc.]." As he grows up, he forgets the original injunction, but he has incorporated it in the Parent of his Child, and he responds as if it were still being said, and stays scared in order to avoid the scary places.

We first came to this realization when we heard patients say, "I am afraid if I get close to an edge of a cliff, [building, etc.] that I will fall off or *jump* off." Now, the only reason the person would jump off is to commit suicide, but for all we can find out, there is not always evidence of depression or suicidal ruminations in him. The only reason he would jump off, if not suicidal, is that he would be responding to some internal message, and when we started looking for it, we found it. Perhaps her father did not catch her once when he threw her up in the air, or his father let him slide down the slide into the water without catching him, so that mother had to jump into the pool to pull him out. These kinds of behavior on the part of parents were interpreted by the patient as "Don't be" injunctions, and he developed a defense by becoming phobic.

It is logical that, if such was the case, then the patient should be able to lose his phobia by deciding he would *never* fall off, jump off, slide off, or slip off. After all, if he is reasonably careful, he doesn't have to be scared to save his life—he just needs to operate from A_2 rather than from P_1, where the original scare is. We treat him by combination of desensitization and redecision work. Sometimes we do the desensitization in fantasy, sometimes in reality.

For instance, if the patient is willing, I will put a ladder against the barn. I will ask the other patients to hold it firmly. I will ask the phobic patient to climb the first step and then tell the others that he is not going to fall off, jump off, or slip off. If he says he is scared, I ask him to step back down on the ground immediately, breathe deeply, get back into not being scared, then climb the first step again. Each time he climbs a higher step without being scared, he repeats the phrase before he climbs higher. When he has reached the top rung, before he climbs onto the roof, I ask him to climb back down, and I go up the ladder onto the roof. Now he is asked to climb up again, and to repeat the phrase again, this time imagining that his parents and his whole original family are below; he is to tell *them* that he is not going to fall off, jump off, slip off, slide off, or lose his balance. I then ask him if he wants to climb on the roof by himself, or wants me to help. I do whichever he wishes, and we now repeat the desensitization as he climbs higher and higher on the sloping roof, until he is standing up on the ridge, looking at the view. He only goes as far as he wants each time, and if he reaches a scary place he goes back, then does it again. In NO CASE has the patient failed to climb up and to drop his fear. If he says that it was too easy, that he was not afraid of things that low, then we find a higher place, such as our log cabin, and do it again. We also do things to hook his Child, so that he is saying the phrase from his Child; for instance, I might ask him to quack at the ducks down on the pond; the ducks will almost always quack back. The patient laughs, and then I ask him to tell the ducks!

Swimming phobias are equally simple and quick. Here the patients are sometimes so afraid that they will not go into the water; others are only scared by deep water. In any case, the technique is to teach them to float, and then to turn over from a prone to a supine float, and then to swim on their backs after they have stabilized. Many patients are afraid of getting water in the mouth, nose, and throat; if so, we play noisy games with face under water, gargle, spit at each other with a mouth full of water, until they laugh and drop that fear. I teach them to float by stabilizing them with my two hands under them, asking them to breathe from deep inspiration to *half*-expiration, and to be aware of how they float on their back off my hands as I am holding them. Then I take one hand off (asking them first if that is OK), then hold them with four fingers, three, two, one, and finally make them aware that they are floating off my finger. This is usually enough for them to drop their fear—especially if the whole workshop is there cheering each move they make. This all may take only five minutes or, in some panicky patients, it may take a little longer. If they cannot float because they are particularly skinny, it is not quite so easy, and I ask them to wear a life belt at first.

At some point I ask them to talk to the water and tell the water that they are in charge, and that they will not let the water drown them. Then I ask them to direct these words to their parents, their siblings. They then swim in from the edge to increasing depths until they are swimming the length of the pool.

If they are sinkers rather than floaters—and very, very few people are sinkers—then I suggest that they always wear some kind of a lifebelt, padded bra, cork jock strap, or something that will give them the bouyancy they need to float. Otherwise, stay out of the water, but stay out by assessment of the danger by the Adult, not because of fear or panic. Usually even the sinker will lose his phobia once he decides not to drown himself or let anyone else drown him.

Summary

In general, we use the same basic methods no matter whom we are treating—the method of getting to the basic impasse as rapidly as possible. Some of the techniques including always using I-Thou transactions: if someone is talking about his wife, about her father, we ask him or her to pretend the other is in the room and to talk to him or her. No matter what was happening, it is difficult to get affect with stories *about* the past, but easy when we bring the past and the person into the room in the now. Of course, we get a contract, but we are not as obsessive about spelling it out as we once were; once we are sure that we and the patient are on the same course, and not in a Parent-Child contract, we start the process for getting to early scenes rapidly, finding the impasse, working through the impasse, and stopping.

We rarely ask, "When was the first time you felt depressed [anxious, phobic, confused]?" Rather, we go back in time progressively as, "What were you depressed about last year?" Then, "How about in medical or graduate school?" Then, "Before that?"—each time getting a short statement in the here-and-now. For instance, the patient says, "When I was in medical school, my father . . ." We stop him. "Tell him this as if he were here." Each time we get the story as if it were happening now, and by the time the patient gets to an early scene, he is in the affect of the scene, is remembering it clearly, and may say, for instance, "If you don't change, I'll kill myself" (if he has been depressed). "What do you say knowing what you know now?" we may ask. In the same Child ego state the patient may say, "You'll never change, and I'm not going to kill myself just because you won't change. I'm not going to kill myself."

And so the redecision is made, and the patient is off to a new start. He, of course, will not give up everything he has done at once, but each time he plays another game and comes to the payoff, he recognizes his part in it and gives up the bad feelings. He also restates the statement that almost always goes with the payoff, about himself and others.

For instance, it might have been, "I'm worthless, and you all are a bunch of bastards to pick on me," which he may change to "Wow, I played 'Kick Me' again, and I see how I did it, and I'm not going to take any payoff; I'm excited about my awareness."

8   Grass, Gobbledygook, and Real *Groovin'*

—R.L.G., M.M.G., and Paul McCormick[1]

A young man went to a three-day group therapy session to work out his problem, which he said was smoking too much grass. He was surrounded by 15 older, better educated men and women, almost all of whom were professional therapists, but who were attending as patients.

The coleaders were Robert L. Goulding and Mary Goulding; the time, early 1969.

The young fellow wore long sideburns, tousled hair almost to his shoulders, awning-striped bell bottoms, a corduroy Edwardian jacket badly torn at the shoulder, and calf-high, rubberized boots, like a car washer's. Most of the professionals seemed pleased when he walked in. He was tall, slim, open-faced and soft-spoken. He appeared shy but friendly. He had a loose pivot tooth, or some kind of faulty dentistry, that caused one of his teeth, when he

---

First appeared in somewhat different form as "Marathon Therapy with a Marijuana 'Loser,'"in *Human Development: Selected Readings,* Morris L. and Natalie R. Haimowitz (Eds.), New York: Crowell, 1973. Used by permission.

[1]Paul McCormick is a counselor in private practice in Stockton, Calif., a teaching member of the International Transactional Analysis Association, and the editor of this book.

smiled, to twist sideways, and once, when he was in the swimming pool, to pop out. His blue eyes were remarkably clear. He'll here be called Joe.

The marathon (with breaks for sleeping) went from Thursday night through Saturday. Joe did not say much until late Friday night, when Bob (Dr. Goulding) asked him, "Do you have something you want to do tonight?"

"Well, I could," he said. "I'm feeling really good. Earlier today, for some reason, I was feeling hostile to the idea of getting rid of this hangup I have. And I was feeling it for quite a little time, although I couldn't really figure out why, other than that it's kind of a groovy hangup to be smoking grass all the time. But, it's an escape, and I set myself up so that I don't [*here he breathed a long sigh*] have enough to do—so that I have lots of free time to sit around, and when I'm stoned, dig myself, just dig existing, and dig doing everyday things. But it was getting to where I found I was needing the stuff too much [*another sigh*] so that I'd be smoking it when, you know, a half an hour later I had something kind of important to do, when I really wouldn't want to be—uh—out of it. But I knew I could handle it just as well out of it as I could straight, because I'm very familiar with the stuff. But it seems that most of what my need is—it seems to mostly come from a combination of the—the excitement, the electricity in my head, kind of dimming down, and the fear of it dimming down more—so that boredom would come. Boredom to me is one of the scariest things I can think of."

Bob: "How'd you stop boredom before you smoked grass?"

Joe: "I didn't really. So pot was a good solution, for a long time. Until I got so familiar with it that the boredom came, even when I was stoned. I've really been trying to work this out for awhile. I've been thinking all about it. But there's a potency I would feel when I was out of it that I didn't feel otherwise. So I was kind of doubting my own potency, and I feel it's—"

Mary: "Would you give an example of where you, quote, 'doubt your own potency?'" *(She wanted a clear description of the problem.)*

Joe: "The potency I doubt is not so much in relationships with other people, although it spread to that for awhile, but—it got to a point where I just said, 'Now to hell with this.' I didn't figure out why. I just said, 'I'm gonna manage it, I'm going to relate with people.' Fine. But the potency I doubt is: Is my own head going to be, and is it now, enough to sustain me—from boredom?"

Mary: "I don't know what that means."

Joe *(long pause)*: "I, I want to avoid, and at the same time bring myself to accept, boredom, if I have to have it. So in a way I'm trying to do two opposite things at the same time. But the main reason: I just felt that my own electrical energy—my thought—isn't enough in itself to keep me from being bored."

Mary *(referring to an earlier session that evening when Bob gave an introductory talk on transactional analysis)*: "Did you dig what Bob said earlier about rackets?"

Joe: "Yes."

(A psychological racket, in TA terms, is the exploiting of a bad feeling, like boredom, or depression, or anger, for use as an excuse to do something a person might not ordinarily do, such as get stoned on marijuana. "Anyone as bored as I am needs something.")

Mary *(wanting to clarify)*: "OK. Boredom's a racket which for some reason or another you've chosen for a long time. I can visualize you in school thinking, 'Teachers, interest me. I'm not in charge of interesting myself,' and they flunked. So you said, 'Well, you guys, I'm bored.'"

Joe: "Yeah."

Mary (*bringing it into the present*): "And I can picture you in your life in Los Angeles saying, 'Something outside of me, come interest me. I choose boredom.'"

Joe: "Yeah."

Mary: "And sometimes you say, 'OK, I'll use something outside of me—grass.'"

Joe: "Yeah. I see that. Intellectually I see it. But I haven't been able to convince myself of my potency to *stop* it."

Mary: "Partly because you use gobbledygook, which I've heard before. You know, it's not just yours—about electricity in heads. As if there's some kind of magical electricity your head doesn't possess. And you know that's sheer fantasy."

Joe (*after a long pause*): "My potency's not showing itself."

Mary: "You're not choosing to be unbored."

Joe: "I don't know *how* to choose to be unbored. I haven't figured out just *how*—other than saying—'All right, listen. I'm going to do it myself.'"

Mary: "That's the only possible way."

Joe: "I haven't been able to do it. I guess that's why I'm here."

Mary: "You haven't chosen yet to be unbored. You're in charge of whether you're bored or not."

Joe (*not sounding convinced*): "Maybe I haven't chosen that at all my levels."

Mary: "I hear you not accepting that you're in charge. So you put it on something magical like electricity, and like grass."

Joe: "I'm only speaking of the effect, you know, the electricity. What it *feels* like."

Mary: "Yeah. But it's as if that weren't you."

Joe (*pause*): "I know—I know it's me."

Mary: "Do you know that you are in charge of whether, and of how much, you're bored?"

Joe *(pause)*: "Yeah, I'm in charge of whether I'm bored or not."

Bob *(another pause)*: "You sure?"

Joe *(pause)*: "Yeah. There is a piece of me resisting, saying, 'Go to the marathon and get some magical—uh—in-touchness with your feelings—'"

Bob: "There's no magic."

Joe: "Yet [*long pause*] I'm scared."

Bob: "What's the scare?"

Joe: "That I can't do it."

Bob: "OK. Then what'll happen?"

Joe: "That I haven't been able to do it. Since the time I realized that—that it's up to me to do it."

Bob *(going for feelings rather than thoughts, so that Joe might re-experience the old fear that led to his deciding that change is dangerous)*: "I *really* want to hear what your scare is. I'm not putting you down."

Joe: "OK."

Bob: "What's the scare."

Joe *(pause)*: "I'm scared that I might not—I should say I'm justifiably scared because I haven't been able to—to have my head in itself—"

Bob: "What's your fantasy of what will happen if you don't use drugs in order not to be bored?"

Joe: "I'll be—in a vacuum."

Bob: "OK. What then?"

Joe: "And it's the vacuum I'm scared of."

Bob: "In your fantasy, let yourself stay in the vacuum for a day, a week, a month—"

Joe: "Like I'm scared—like I'm on a downhill escalator, vacuum-wise, or in a big bell jar, with the air slowly pulling out."

Bob: "OK. At the bottom of the escalator there's a level spot. What happens then?"

Joe: "That's the vacuum. And I don't dig it."

Bob *(still going for something concrete)*: "What's the vacuum like?"

Joe: "The vacuum?"

Bob: "Vacuum means nothing. There you are, Joe. Arms, legs, body, head, chest, heart, penis—the works. You're not a vacuum."

Joe: "Yeah, it means I have a body, but I'm not satisfied with the—way I think."

Bob: "Now you're down at the bottom of the escalator. You're on the level, on the basement floor. You feel like a vacuum, there are no drugs. What do you do now?"

Joe: "Rot."

Bob: "Huh?"

Joe: "Rot."

Bob: "Rot?"

Joe: "Rot."

Bob *(once more)*: "Rot?"

Joe: "Well, that's my fantasy."

Bob: "Tell me about your rotting. There you are lying on the cement floor, rotting away, for a day, a week, a month—what are you going to do?" *(Bob was encouraging him to go on with the fantasy to its completion, to see if he foresaw the ending, and wanted to change it.)*

Joe: "I do things that interest me."

Bob: "Like what?"

Joe: "Like film."

Mary: "Go on."

Joe: "So I *film.*"

Bob: "OK."

Joe: "And—you know, get involved with people, and all that."

Bob: "So you got off the floor and went up the up-escalator, huh? You find some people—"

Joe: "But I'm not *seeing* it as going up the escalator. I see it as a diversion from the cosmic rottenness."

Mary *(being tough Adult)*: "You're back to gobbledygook."

Joe: "That's the way I see it."

Bob: "OK. So what pot does is keep the cosmic rottenness from getting you, huh?"

Joe: "Yeah, it keeps it from getting me."

Bob: "That sound pretty magical to you?"

Joe: "Uh [*pause*] no. It sound more biologic. I mean, like it turns on my head."

Mary: "One more fantasy trip. OK?"

Joe: "Yeah."

Mary: "You go home from this marathon to Katie [*Joe's wife*] and you say, 'Well, it didn't work;' and then you light up."

Joe: "Yeah, that's about it."

Mary: "And, as you light up, what does Katie say?"

Joe: "Well, it's a drag—it's a drag [*he laughs*] between us. Because—she doesn't dig grass as much as I do."

Mary *(wanting to check her hunch that Joe's Child ego state has already decided that he probably won't change anything at the marathon)*: "OK. You go back to Katie and you say, 'Well, it didn't work,' and you light up. What's Katie say?"

Joe: "She's—she's disappointed, and—she doesn't dig it."

Mary: "And you?"

Joe: "And me?"

Mary *(wondering if Joe's Child is already feeling a little triumphant for "proving" that the marathon won't change anything)*: "Yeah. What do you feel?"

Joe: "I'm feeling—I'm feeling, 'Man, here comes the vacuum.'"

Mary: "As you light up?"

Joe: "No. As I light up I think, 'Bye bye vacuum.'"

(Bob has started to put on the board a time-space diagram showing the line from birth to death, the horizontal line representing time, and the vertical line representing place, so that the intersection is the here-and-now. The time scale goes from zero to X, representing an unknown ending.)

Joe *(looking at the board)*: "And I don't see it as any kind of suicide. I don't feel that, at all."

Bob: "Rot? Cosmic rot? What's that?"

Joe: "Cosmic rot is *not* suicide. It's life. But it's not what I dig."

Bob *(back at the time-space diagram)*: "You see, we didn't get to where you'd be in 10 years, 15 years, 20 years, with cosmic rot. We got off that."

Joe: "Yes, that would kind of be—that's as far as I can see it."

Mary: "You been on hard stuff?" *(Bob and Mary believe that use of hard stuff, especially by injection, is more often than not an indicator of a suicidal script.)*

Joe: "I've had some mescaline."

Bob: "That's all?"

Joe: "I had some speed, once. Only for the sake of experimenting. Like I flew into a city to take it. And before I'd really get to need it, I split the city, to where I couldn't get any more. It was hell. You know, coming down, and all that. If I'd stayed in the city I would have taken more. And I purposely didn't."

Bob: "Any heroin?"

Joe: "No, no, because I wouldn't want to."

Mary: "That mean you won't?"

Joe: "I won't. I like—trippy stuff."

Bob: "Acid?"

Joe: "I'd like to."

Bob: "Acid?"

Joe: "Yes. I haven't but I'd like to."

Bob *(pause)*: "OK."

Mary *(to Bob)*: "You want to follow my thing?"

Bob: "Yes. [*then to Joe*] 'OK' doesn't mean it's OK to take acid. It means I don't know where to go right now."

Mary: "I want to follow my thing, because I've got a hunch that if we don't make this explicit we may be in a con game. I have a hunch that Katie sent you here—"

Joe: "In a way."

Mary: "—so you'll reform, and I've got a hunch that's a big old game; because I think your Kid [Child ego state] knows how to screw Parents [Parent ego states] [*pause*]. It really doesn't affect my life, you know, whether you use grass or not" *(letting Joe know she is not going to play Rescuer)*.

Joe: "Yeah, I know."

Mary: "Do you?"

Joe: "And I see myself—you know, still using it even after this—what I *want* is, I still want to use grass, but I don't want to have the need—"

Bob: "If tomorrow [*it's now late at night*] you and I agree that we will not discuss electricity in your head, and we'll not discuss cosmic rot, and we'll not discuss grass, will you come up with a contract [*a mutually-agreed-on course of action toward a clearly defined treatment goal*] that we can work with here? Because I can't work with cosmic rot, and I can't work with electricity in your head, and I don't want to work with grass. But I'd like to work with you. Will you find another contract besides those three, and tell me what it is in the morning?"

Joe: "Yeah. Yeah, I can do that."

(If a patient wants to quit a drug, Bob and Mary ask, "When?" If he says, "Right now," they say, "Great. Now what do you want to work on?" If therapists are not tough about that, users will probably hook them into a rescuer, persecutor, or patsy role in the drug game. Since Joe had not said he wanted to quit grass, little could have been gained by discussing the stuff.)

Bob: "OK—Where are you, Dan?"

Dan: "I'm really kind of turned off, Bob. I felt we've been kind of conned. . . .I feel I'm not getting into anything . . . and I'm not sure why."

Bob: "Want to let it go for tonight?"

Dan: "Yeah."

Bob *(looking at Mary)*: "I'm ready to let it all go tonight. I'm getting pretty tired."

Mary: "OK."

Bob: "But I'm willing to go on with anybody who has anything urgent to work on tonight."

Joe: "I'm really feeling hanging. I mean—I'm not trying to con you."

Bob: "I'm not accusing you of anything, Joe. I'm not saying you're in a procedure or a maneuver [*Adult moves*] where you're conning me. I'm saying that your Child, outside of your Adult awareness, *may be* involved in a con, and I don't want to be in a game. So I'd like to deal with things you have to deal with besides those three specific complaints you mentioned. I think we can get somewhere, but not arguing about cosmic rot. OK?"

Joe: "But—but it seems like it's in that dimension."

Bob: "OK [*with a friendly chuckle*]. OK. Will you sleep on it?"

Joe: "Yeah."

(The next morning, with the group assembled to start the last day of the marathon.)

Mary: "Joe, we left you thinking last night."

Joe: "Yeah. And—this morning I think I figured out a different way—a different contract. I want to find out what in me is holding me back from being enthusiastic."

Mary: "Hey!"

Bob: "That one I can understand, and hear, and work with!—and once you've found out, what then?"

Joe: "Once I found out, then I could see it coming up on me, and I could say 'Ah ha, I know you. Go back to hell.' So far, I haven't been able to figure out what or who in me it is."

Mary: "Can you pinpoint any time in your life when you stopped being enthusiastic?" (*Mary was going for the "rubber band," the snapping back to an earlier experience that may have led to his deciding that enthusiasm does not pay.*)

Joe: "Well, like I say, it's been kind of diminishing. As a little kid, and as a bigger kid, I could get really involved in whatever I was doing."

Mary: "What were you enthusiastic about when you were a little kid?"

Joe: "Oh, just everything. I was alone a lot because I had two much older brothers, and they were either at school, or living away at school, so I was pretty much an only child. And my parents, my mother was unenthusiastic about what I—whatever I would do, and—she was a cold fish. My father, on the other hand, he'd be more enthusiastic. When I'd come bouncing up to him, he'd respond to me. But she wouldn't. And so I spent pretty much all my time alone, outside. We lived on a big—in the country, and all that. So I was able to be kind of one with nature."

Mary: "And then?"

Joe: "Then I moved into town. It wasn't city or anything, but it was away from the country, and I wanted to go back. I mean I'd hound 'em for weeks. I was eighth grade so I was pretty old. I really missed the country. The country was kind of where my [*sigh*] spirit was. And once I moved into town, I never could really get back to the country. I'd go back out there, but it was over for me."

Mary: "What was the country? Farm? Animals?"

Joe: "It was Kansas. It was flat. There were some animals around, although not on our farm. We kind of had a farm, but we didn't do anything with it. We just had the acreage, and fields, with little trees around, and some big trees, woods, and a river going through. It was ideal. Really ideal. And then we moved. And it was at that point, I suppose—that was the really important point."

Mary: "You became a town kid instead of a country kid. Same school?"

Joe: "Yeah, same school. Same friends. I lived in town only for one year, though, and then I was shipped off to boarding school."

Mary: "How come?"

("How come?" is more likely to be heard and responded to by a non-accused-feeling Child than is the more Parental "Why?" which often evokes Child defensiveness.)

Joe: "Because in Claremont Park you—"

Mary: "You said Claremont Park? OK. I know the place [*laughing*]."

Joe: "In Claremont Park you go the local school, and then you go to boarding school."

Mary (*laughing*): "That's right; I come from Isleton. You know where that is?"

Joe: "Yeah. I lived in Woodford, and then moved into Claremont Park."

Mary: "So, ever get your enthusiasm up for boarding school?"

Joe: "No. Uh uh. I spent two years in a school, in the East, that was very conservative. I just didn't like it at all. And my grades were no good, so they had me in day-and-night study hall. I never had any time to myself except a couple of hours a day they'd give you for free time. Probably even less than that. I was kind of trapped for two years there, but at that point I wasn't outspoken about it. I just kind of flubbed along there until I was finally bounced out. Then I went to Middle Meadow School in the Southwest, and there we were on a big prairie. 1500 acres, cattle, and it was, you know, there I was in the country. Mountains, and all that, but like I'd already lost my enthusiasm for nature, and I guess—for my own head."

Mary: "When you came back home from boarding school—it sounds like you were very unhappy those two years. Were you?"

Joe: "Yes. I'd be unhappy, but it wasn't—yes. I was unhappy."

Mary: "How'd you present that to your folks, on vacations, in summer? Did you make any attempts not to go back?"

Joe: "Not really—as I was growing up it was better not to analyze any kind of situation. I never really analyzed boarding school. I just kinda said, 'Oh, it's all right,' you know, and never say anything against it. Although I did make it clear that I wasn't jumping up and down about it. But at that point I didn't see any other path for me."

Mary: "What did you do in the study halls?"

Joe: "Shat off." *(Laughter from the whole group.)*

Mary: "What's that?"

Joe: "Oh, you know. The past tense of shit. I sat there and picked my nose. It was *boring.* Oh—study hall! And they had me in there for hours—"

Bob: "How did you manage that?" *(Bob wanted to challenge Joe's "they had me in there," to alert him that a part of him, at least, had set it up that way.)*

Joe: "How did I *manage* it?"

Bob: "Yeah. How did you manage getting in study hall all those hours—and then saying, 'Gee, I hated all that, all those boring hours'? Somehow you kept landing there."

Joe: "The work was hard. And—I didn't like the school enough really to want to work."

Bob: "So in effect you said, 'I'll show you guys. I'll just not work, and I'll go to study hall every day.'"

(This was an attempt by Bob to see if Joe was at all aware of his "Ain't It Awful" game, which he played without Adult deliberation; but Joe was not yet buying it.)

Joe: "No, not so much that as just—uh—it was the lesser of two evils."

Mary: "What was the bigger evil?"

Joe: "The bigger evil was—uh—the kind of insurmountable mountain of getting good grades at that school. 'Cause you know, for some teachers I'd really try, and my grades still wouldn't be so good. Oh, it was a tough school. And my study habits, even when I wanted to learn something, weren't that good. I guess I just kind of sat there and let the thoughts go in my head and go right out again. You know. So I can't remember anything."

Bob: "I just got a fantasy of a thought machine. When you were in study hall, every once in a while you'd open up a flap in your head, and thoughts would come in. And you had a flap over here, where they'd come out again."

Joe *(not getting the point)*: "Yeah. It was an effortless kind of existence, sitting there. I'd just kind of sit, and thoughts would come in and go out."

Bob: "You really believe that? Thoughts came in and went out?"

Joe *(seriously)*: "Yes. Yes."

Mary: "That's part of what we were talking about last night. Your feeling of not being in charge."

Joe: "Yeah. That's what they did and—uh—"

(Bob and Mary both chuckled, and waited a moment for Joe's Adult to get the point, but his Child was resisting admitting responsibility for his own thoughts.)

Mary: "You really, really, *really* don't believe that you choose your own thoughts."

(long pause.)

Joe: "Yeah—I haven't done that. I'm not denying that it can be done."

Mary: "Who has? Who has, for you?"

Bob: "If you don't choose them, who does?"

Joe: "Well—I'd choose my own thoughts, but they were so—*I* was so dull—I felt so dull and bored, for those two years, that I'd think them and I wouldn't retain them, at all. That's what I mean by going in and out."

Mary: "And then you went to the Southwest, to school?"

Joe: "Yeah."

Mary: "And then what?"

Joe: "Educationally, I was so behind by the time I got there that even though it was a better place, and I have a lot of really good feelings for the school—like I started a film festival there—and I'm going back for it next month."

Mary: "Oh! So you did arouse yourself from being apathetic?"

Joe: "Yes, in some areas. Not much scholastically, though."

Mary: "But in areas of importance to you, you did?"

Joe: "Yeah. I started filming."

Mary: "So you were enthusiastic at those points? When you were filming, and when you were organizing a film festival?"

Joe: "Right. Right. There was a time when I got going so much—the film festival was coming up, and I was in this play, and all these other things were going on, that

I just kind of ran myself into the ground and got mono [*mononucleosis*]. Although I'm not feeling, you know, if I get enthusiastic I'll get mono. I'm just saying this is what happened. I was really enthusiastic about the few things I was interested in, and—I didn't get much sleep then. The hours I was sleeping were maybe from two to seven every morning for a long time. Of course, Katie had come to visit me the week before. She might have been carrying it around with her." *(Laughter from the group.)*

Bob: "OK. So at a certain point in your life, when you were at school in the East, you felt it was easy to choose boredom over enthusiasm."

Joe: "Huh?"

Bob: "It was easier to choose boredom over enthusiasm when you were East? There was that 'insurmountable mountain' in your studies."

Joe: "Yes. And also, the people at that school were not ones I'd get enthusiastic about."

Bob: "And you're still maintaining the position that it's easier to choose boredom over enthusiasm."

Joe: "Huh? Yeah, and I suppose what has happened is that the 'easier to choose' has gotten—you know, the 'easier to choose to be bored' has gotten so that it's insurmountably difficult to become enthusiastic."

Bob: "Insurmountably?"

Joe: "Well, you know, that's the way I felt. It doesn't seem like it now."

Mary: "Are you enthusiastic now, when you're filming? You *are* filming now?"

Joe: "Yes."

Mary: "Are you enthusiastic when you're doing that?"

Joe: "Yes."

Bob *(to see if Joe would feel enthusiastic in the room, right now)*: "What do you film, Joe?"

Joe *(not with enthusiasm)*: "I film shorts, entertainment shorts. The only trouble I suppose with the filming is that—it's expensive, and so I can't film all the time. I can only film you know, a roll of film a week or so. Sometimes more, sometimes less, and so it doesn't occupy all my time; and I suppose I've let myself get into a kind of bored limbo in other areas. I mean, at other times."

Mary: "Does that mean if you're going to film as much as you want to, you're going to have to have a second job?"

Joe: "Yeah, so recently I've been getting going onto a job, although I haven't got one yet. You know, I've started walking the streets looking for one. Guess 'cause I was gettin' bored with being bored."

Bob *(stopping the recorder and running the tape back a bit)*: "I want you to hear something you said, Joe."

Recorder: ". . .I've let myself get into a kind of bored limbo . . ." *(Again,)* ". . . I've let myself get into a kind of bored limbo . . ." *(And again.)* ". . . I've let myself get into a kind of bored limbo . . ."

Bob: "So you let yourself get into the limbo, and you also let yourself get out." *(Bob was alerting Joe to his acknowledgement that he really is responsible for his own boredom.)*

Joe: "Yeah."

Bob: "How are you going to continue to do that?—You already said some things. You're looking for another job so you'll have more money available to make more film. What else can you do besides that?"

Joe *(pause)*: "Well, I can, you know, dig things around me, although—part of me's been saying, 'Hey, don't dig it.'"

Bob: "OK. Stay with the 'dig.' Last night you were digging the sky. You were enjoying."

Joe: "Yea. I was digging it—I suppose some of it may be competition with Katie, maybe a competition thing I have in my head with her. Because when I met her I was kind of in a—I met her right after I was at boarding school in the East, with study halls and everything, and I was in bad-news condition. At one point, I, uh—"

Bob: "Hey, will you right now stay with the things you're enthusiastic about? I've been hearing about how you're enthusiastic about filming, about getting another job. Are you?"

Joe: "Yes."

Bob: "Are you enthusiastic about the things you see around you? Will you tell us about it?"

Joe: "But I was trying to explain what's holding me back."

Bob: "Yeah, I know."

Joe *(looking out the window)*: "You know, if I want to get enthusiastic about the hills over there—about my being here today—there has been a piece of me saying, 'Don't do it.' And I don't know if it is only the piece of me that says, 'It's too hard to get enthusiastic about it,' or if it's also the competition thing because—

"When I met her I was down, and she was enthusiastic. She's a very enthusiastic person, and I kind of absorbed it through *her*; and in that way I think I might have gotten into a kind of competition thing with her. You know, as if the competition with her is my motive. She'd end up being enthusiastic, and I'd be as enthusiastic. That kind of thing. And I know, 'What's the race?' You know, what's the point of that?"

Bob: "What is?"

Joe: "There's none."

Bob: "You sure?"

Joe: "Of being in competition with her, there's none. [*Pause*] But the things I'm enthusiastic about. Back to that—I'm enthusiastic about the kids. About the baby coming up. I'm all excited about that. And uh—that's about it in Los Angeles.

"I haven't until just recently allowed myself to become enthusiastic about other things. I've been kind of hibernating up in the dark room, doing a lot of experiments with film. And although I've been learning from the experiments, I've been kind of wallowing in, you know, kind of spending *much* too much time up there, in the dark room, instead of going out and turning on my exploratory urge. I've been keeping it quiet."

Mary: "You mean, just sitting up there?"

Joe: "Yea. I've been *doing* things. And I've been content up there. But it's not enough. So that's why I've recently started going out more."

Bob: "You mean, coming out of the dark, huh?"

Joe: "Yeah, Yeah."

Mary: "Do you and Katie have friends?"

Joe: "Yeah."

Mary: "And that's OK?"

Joe: "Yeah. That's OK."

Mary: "You can be enthusiastic about friends?"

Joe: "Yeah. We don't have too many yet, because right after we moved, she got pregnant, and was really sick for awhile. She just hasn't felt like making too many. And I don't project myself to make friends too much—and that's OK. I just don't push it as much as she would. She would make the friends, and once—she'd be out at Flub—you know, like Eileen Feather's place, you know, shake things? She'd be at Flub, and she'd bring people back from Flub." *(Laughter from the whole group.)*

One of the women asked: "What's Flub?"

Joe: "Oh! Do I ever like to talk about Flub! [*More laughter*] Flub is a placed called the Slenderize Salon for Women. They have all sorts of machines, and belts, and vibrators, and everything like that. Well, she goes there. She does her legs, and her chin [*much laughter from the women*]."

Joe: "But anyway, she'll be out making the friends and bringing them back, and I'll be choosing, from the ones who come in, the friends I want. And it's been comfortable because I'm kind of shy to just go up to someone and, you know, become a friend."

Bob: "Are you?"

Joe: "Yeah."

Dan: "I was kind of impressed, Joe, yesterday, about what I thought was a lack of enthusiasm for your own films. You spoke to me about your films enthusiastically, but when I told you I had a friend, a film distributor, who might be interested (although, I couldn't answer for him, but it is a lead), you didn't seem to be enthusiastic about that. I thought you were putting me off. It was almost like *I* had to sell *you*. Of course, I didn't want to make it a hard sell."

Joe: "Yeah. Uh—that's been something—I've been scared to project my films to distributors. I really don't know why. It was heavy for awhile. You know, I just didn't—I wanted to make the films, and just have them be me. I didn't want to show them to other people—other than my friends, because that was safe, with friends. I suppose because—well, some people would think it was no good, the film. And so—uh—"

Bob: "It's kind of like talking about you. 'I'm afraid to show myself to people; I'm afraid to show my films to people.'"

Joe: "Yeah, Yeah, I'm afraid to show myself. Like—uh—I wanted to distribute a movie, and it took me months to get to the yellow pages to look for a distributor. I finally went to one, and he looked at it and didn't want it, so I stopped it at that. I haven't gone to any others—because I've been scared to."

Bob: "What—what—what's the magic? You don't show yourself, or your films, to people. What's that preventing?"

Joe *(pause)*: "It's preventing me from—from coming out of this kind of womb I think I've been living in."

Mary: "That's your Adult, but what's your Child say?" *(Mary's hunch was that retreating to the womb was too sophisticated a notion to be a Child expression.)*

Joe: "My Child says that he doesn't want to."

Bob: "What's your fantasy of what will happen if you show your films, show yourself, to all the distributors in the world? [*Pause.*] Get with your Child. Get with your fantasies. [*Pause.*] What horrible things might happen if you show the good things you have?"

Joe: "I've never thought of it that way. I've always, you know, not liked to show people—and—I think I'm kind of feeling that if I *show*—uh—I may find out that filming is not the thing for me, but I really want it to be the thing for me—'cause I want to do it."

Bob *(believing that Joe's Child decision to hide out was probably made long before he started filming)*: "OK. Let's go back before filming."

Joe: "So I guess I'm scared that if I find filming is not for me, I've nothing."

Mary: "OK. Can you take that back to grade school? Pick a scene in grade school."

Joe: "Pick a scene?"

Mary: "Yeah. In your grade school days, at home or in school, were you enthusiastic about something you'd been doing?"

Bob *(pause)*: "What bad will happen if you let the rest of the world know about you? You're a little kid."

Joe: "I suppose the rest of the world would think—uh—the kid's really not skilled, or the kid's done a lousy job. It's the Kid. I'm looking at myself not as Adult."

(Mary started to say something and Bob intervened): "Let's take it to before films. What was the fear of what people would, or—what would happen to you if you said, 'Hey! I'm Joe; I just found something beautiful!'"

Joe: "My mother would be unenthusiastic."

Bob: "And?"

Mary: "What would she do? Put her right here. [*Mary outlined with both hands the imaginary figure of Joe's mother standing there in the room.*] Suppose Joe's standing here with a picture he's just colored?"

Joe: "I really don't remember *showing* anything to her. I would keep it to myself."

Bob: "That's why I asked you to fantasize. What would happen if you showed it to her? If you suddenly turned off your boredom and got enthusiastic?"

Joe: "And showed something to her?"

Bob: "Yeah."

Joe: "Well, when I was a kid, I'd get enthusiastic, and I wouldn't show it to—*her*. If I showed it to her she'd give a tight-lipped smile like this. Uptight. 'That's nice.' [*Imitating his mother.*] She wouldn't knock it—just, you know—it would be a stifled—uh, 'Nice.'"

Mary: "And your brothers?"

Joe: "They weren't home too much. I looked at my brothers, because they were like nine or ten years older than me, I looked at them as other adults."

Mary: "In your fantasy, your brothers are off in boarding school?"

Joe: "Yeah. Since the time I was about five."

Mary: "Before they went off, if you showed them a picture?"

Joe: "Their reaction would be—I see them reacting—'Oh, that's a little kid picture. And I'm a *big* kid, and you're not big.'"

Bob: "Then what do they do?"

Joe: "That's all. It was just a little kid picture. Yeah—and that's all."

Mary (*sensing from his softened voice and slumped posture that he was re-experiencing the four-year-old Child in himself*): "And how do you respond to them, when you're four?"

Joe (*sadly*): "I'd be sad."

Ruby (*pause*): "And did you like the picture much after that?"

Joe: "No."

Bob: "So the magic is: You won't show yourself, or you won't show your films—you won't show them what you've got, your creativity, your—"

Joe: "*I'll* still like 'em."

Bob: "Yeah. *You'll* still like 'em. But if you show them to anybody, they'll crumble into dust. Into cosmic rot."

Joe (*pause; then sadly*): "Yeah."

Bob: "That really true?"

Joe: "Huh?—No."

Bob: "What's the worst thing that can happen, Joe, if the rest of the world doesn't dig your pictures, your films?"

Joe: "Nothing too terrible—because I'd feel like—it's with writing books. I've only started filming just a few years ago, and recently started doing my things to *show* them to people, and all that, so, you know, I am relatively inexperienced. So I feel that even if nobody digs the stuff *now*, the time's going to come when I do somethin' out of sight!"

Bob (*laughing softly*): "OK."

Mary: "You going to be showing it?"

Joe: "Huh?"

Mary: "You going to be showing it?"

Joe: "Yeah." *(With a smile.)*

(Mary laughed warmly.)

Bob: "OK"

Viola *(to Joe)*: "You *are* out of sight."

Mary: "I hear the basic slogan that you labored under. It's that you're not important. In some ways you weren't important to your mother, or important to your brothers. And, I'm imagining, not too important to your classmates. Or were you?"

Joe: "No. I didn't have too many friends because I was kind of—I lived farther away than anybody else from the school, so I wouldn't see anybody after—and, uh, I went through grade school pretty much as the joker. I'm thinking of the latter part of grade school."

Mary: "By 'joker,' you mean the one who pulled jokes, or the one who as was laughed at?"

Joe: "It'd be a combination."

Ruby: "The extra card in the deck?"

Joe: "Huh?"

Ruby: "The extra card in the deck?"

Joe: "Yeah."

Bob *(to Ruby)*: [*Chuckle*] "Good for you."

Joe: "Yeah. Yeah—kind of."

Dan: "My association was to The Joker in that TV show."

Viola: "Bat Man?"

Dan: "Bat Man. You know, kind of an evil cat."

Joe: "No—no. Kind of, if anything serious was going on—I wouldn't destroy it or anything—I'd project a kind of humorous slant to it, to make it less important." *(From his Parent he discounts himself and others. In his Child he feels discounted.)*

Bob: "Less close."

Joe *(agreeing)*: "Less close."

Viola: "Did your brothers attend the same school?"

Joe: "No, they both started off at Waltham School, which was the same type of strict deal. One stayed and graduated from there, but he was well known to the headmaster and some of the teachers at my boarding school. So, to the teachers I came to school as Eddie's brother, not as me. And—uh—when I got to Middle Meadow—it was just me. And I realized that, towards the end of my last year in the East, I realized that at a new school next year I can be anyone I want to be. I can be tough, I can be phoney, I can be nice—and as it worked out when I got there I didn't make any effort, and I was just *myself.*"

While Joe was talking, Bob was at the blackboard diagramming Joe's "life script matrix," the starting place of the life decisions Joe made for himself when he was very young.

The life script hypothesis, according to Berne, and verified again and again in Bob and Mary's clinical experience, is that a person decides in early childhood how he is going to transact life's business long before he is experienced or judicious enough to make such a long-term commitment. His severely limited milieu, his matrix for assessing what goes on in the world and what he's going to do about it, is restricted primarily to the social transactions, first nonverbal, and then verbal, within his own family. The strongest influence appears to come from the Child (the most feeling of the three ego states) of the nurturing parent, who is usually the mother. Her physical handling of the infant, and her manifestations of approval and disapproval, her smiles and frowns, convey to him what she expects of him. If her Child ego state is uncomfortable, for example, with physical closeness, she will let him know, one way or another. The Parent in her may occasionally say, "Come and kiss your mother good night," but her physically cool reception of his embrace will say, even louder, "But don't come too close." The boy, strongly dependent on her for the nurturing he does get, assures himself of a continuance of that nurturing by complying with her Child demands. Perhaps completely outside of her Adult awareness, she may repeatedly reinforce a destructive message such as, "Don't be comfortable with closeness," until he decides he had better abide by her prohibition. Defying the prohibition may result in so distressing a visceral discomfort (after all, he is threatening to cut off his own milk supply) that he submits, and stops warming up to people. From then on he may be said to have an aloof character, or that he is "by nature" distant, whereas, according to Berne, his own early decision not to be close is the main basis of his character. Decisions, even forgotten ones, no matter how strongly encouraged by early parental programming, are self-determined, and at least to some extent reversible. In any event, as far as a patient in treatment is concerned, the only things worth working on are the changeables, so instead of fretting about who was really responsible for destructive early decisions, the therapist and patient address themselves to whatever available options for change there are. Even if the don't-get-close person never decides to drop his aloofness entirely, he may decide to stop setting people up to let him down, a game he may have been playing for years to reinforce his people-are-not-OK stance. He can decide to devote his energies to more productive enterprises, and at least adapt, if not entirely change, his delimiting script.

TA therapists listen carefully for both constructive and destructive parental injunctions, and alert the patient to them by drawing the script matrix (Steiner, 1966) on the board. The diagram shows the mother's and father's Parent and Child messages to the offspring. In its simplest form, it indicates the most common Parent messages from mother and daddy as going to, and being assimilated by, the Parent ego state of the son or daughter. The Child messages of the parents are shown as directed to the Child in the offspring. The Parent messages are usually defensible although often moralistic commands such as "Grow up," "Behave yourself," "Make money," "Present a good appearance," "Get an education," and so forth. Frequently, they have more to do with how the mother and father want the world to see their offspring than with granting autonomy or freedom of choice to the youngster. Parental commands are often prejudicial; for example, "Be seen with the right people."

The messages from the Child *ego states of mother and dad are more significant as influences on the character formation of the baby. He* really *hears what mommy and daddy, from their viscera,* don't *want him to do. If their Child ego states are uncomfortable with spontaneity, or creativity, or genius, or competition, their frowns and other signs of displeasure will get the word through to him very quickly, not to be too bright, too charming, too competitive, or too successful. These prohibitions are sometimes called witch messages. When mother's and dad's Child (not Parent) messages are injunctions against failure, or mediocrity, or apathy, or passivity, they are not witch messages. They are grants of permission to succeed, to enjoy, to live.*

Bob drew a diagram (figure 4) on the board, and eventually filled in the messages.

Bob: (at the board): "Did your father have any kind of enthusiasm?"

Joe: "Yeah."

Mary: "What was he enthusiastic about?"

Joe: "He was enthusiastic about—he was great around the kids about—teaching me things, games. He taught me, or had me learn, everything. You know, bridge, golf,

Figure 4

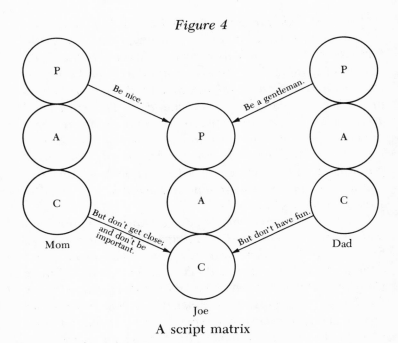

A script matrix

tennis, backgammon: games. And so he—he's enthusiastic, although he was very—he's kind of on the straight road, would never veer off. Doesn't understand creativity too much."

Mary: "Is he enthusiastic about his own work."

Joe: "Yes, he is. He's *not* enthusiastic about, uh—coming home. He'd come home and the whole thing was a routine. You know, he'd come home, have his drink, have dinner. He'd ask the same question every night at the dinner table. The three of us there; five of us if my brothers were home. 'Well, what did you do today?' I'd say 'such and such' and he'd say, 'That's nice,' and then start talking to Mom back and forth. And they'd bicker at each other."

Bob (*still at the board*): "So Mom said, 'Don't be enthusiastic,' and 'Don't get close,' in all kinds of ways. Your father says, 'Learn routines, learn things well, but don't be too enthusiastic about enjoying too much.' Because he really wasn't too creative or too enthusiastic, huh?"

Joe: "Yeah. It was more—'You learn because there's nothing else to do.' I mean, 'There's no other way to do it.'"

Bob (*pointing on the script matrix to dad's messages*): "That's why I put this here. 'Learn routine things, like bridge, backgammon, tennis—'"

Joe: "Yeah."

Bob: "—and be a gentleman, but don't be enthusiastic about it.' Because he really wasn't enthusiastic, was he?"

Ruby: "Don't be inventive."

Joe (*to Bob*): "He was about the things he taught me. [*Then, to Ruby*] Don't be inventive. Yeah!"

Mary: "That's how come, I would guess, how come it's easy for you to be enthusiastic about Katie's son [*by a previous marriage*]—You said that you really dug the boy."

Joe: "Yeah. Yeah."

Mary: "And I assume that's the part, the good part, that you got from your father."

Joe: "Yeah, because he dug me as a little kid."

Mary: "Yeah. Exactly."

Joe: "Yeah."

Bob: "OK. So, if you do become enthusiastic about your films, about showing yourself to the rest of the world, you're going to be disobeying your mother's bad messages. Is that safe?"

Joe: "Yeah. That's safe, and that's something I've accepted. Before I hadn't really looked at it with my brothers coming in, also."

Bob: "So it's safe now to be enthusiastic?"

Joe: "Yeah."

Bob: "You sure?"

Joe: "Yeah."

Mary: "OK. Now I'll bring in grass again, huh? Because one of the things about grass is, even if people do it in a big crowd, it's really a lonely trip. It's colored pictures in your own head you don't have to show anybody. Know what I mean?"

Joe: "Yeah."

Mary: "And I think that it fits in with the message, 'Don't get close.'"

Joe: "Correct. Yeah. I still dig the colored pictures, but now I don't have to just stay only with them."

Mary: "Yeah—because they're something you can't show. See the importance?"

(Joe nodded affirmatively and smiled toward Dan.)

Bob: "Who were you smiling at then? At Dan?"

Joe: "Yeah."

Dan: "Yeah, I quickly feel in contact with him. Last night we weren't."

Joe: "Yeah—'cause I was scared."

Fred: "Joe, have you sold any of your films yet?"

Joe: "No."

Fred: "How long have you been at it?"

Joe: "About—most of the work I've done has been for festivals. And I would show films in festivals. And I've won. I've won one festival two years in a row. My films are pretty good, actually, because I've taken two first prizes, in the 8 and 16mm division." *(At this point he was genuinely enthusiastic in voice, expression, and gesture.)*

(Bob chuckled. These spontaneous chuckles from Bob and Mary, they believe, are intuitively-timed bestowals of "permission" [Crossman, 1966] to their patients to see themselves as OK, and to enjoy their own successes.)

Mary: "OK, so a lonely little kid who was told he wasn't important, who kept his things to himself, would play an interesting sleeping beauty. And I hear you playing a sleeping beauty about your films. Like maybe some distributor will find you in your tower in the thorns."

Joe: "Yeah," *(and he laughed, along with the whole group).*

Mary: "You're going to reverse that, huh?"

Joe: "Yeah."

Fred: "What's it mean to win a festival? I'm not familiar with that."

Joe: "A whole bunch of people will enter their films into one festival, and they'll show the festival to an audience, and also to judges. And the judges pick which they think is the best film."

Fred: "A lot of competition."

Joe: "Sometimes it is, sometime not, depending on the festival."

Fred: "So, you haven't hidden them as much as it sounds—earlier."

Bob: "OK [*chuckle*] Now, do you understand, Fred, why I didn't push Joe last night?"

Fred: "Yes, it was getting late. I—"

Bob: "Not just that. I wanted *him* to get at it."

Fred: "Right."

Bob *(to Joe)*: "Because I suspected that one of the things that you do, Joseph, is suck people into pushing you. Then you can push them back. Is that true?"

Joe: "Yeah." *(thoughtfully)*

Bob (to Joe): "I like what you did this morning. You got down to the nub of it, the point of the problem. And you dealt with it in a nice clear and concise way."

Joe: "Yeah. Thank you."

Mary: "You did a beautiful job today."

(That evening, as the marathon was ending, Mary said):
"So, Joe, would you start, and go around, and each of you
say what your redecision is? What you're going to do, or
be, for you?"

Joe: "My redecision is this: It's that my head is OK—
as it is."

Mary: "Wow!"

Bob: "It sure is."

Joe: "I guess that sums it up. Everything else is an
extension of that."

Bob *(chuckling)*: "It sure is."

*(At the marathon-ending party later that night, Joe, in
his unpushy, gracious way, was everywhere. He folk-
danced with the women; played Bob's set of drums; accompanied on Bob's clarinet, in harmony, a recording of
Johnny Dodd's jazz clarinet; and chatted enthusiastically
with everyone there.)*

Two and a half months later Joe said, "The marathon
was constructive. Especially my realization of the effect
my brothers had on me. I was already fairly aware of the
effect my parents had on me, but even that became
clearer in the marathon. Afterwards, I realized that my
brothers had much more influence on me than I'd
thought. They were like an additional set of adults in the
house, so their influence was strong. I was able to see it
for the first time, and junk the bad influence once I saw
it.

"You know, I've recalled that there really was a colored
picture. Once, when my oldest brother, who I got along
better with, and I were to go fishing early in the morning,
when I was about eight, I drew him a picture. I don't
know why I associated it with the message I wrote on it,
but it was a picture of a western scene. Two gunmen having it out, one of them getting shot, and the other one

shooting him. It was quite a good picture. At the top of it it said WAKE ME UP. So that he wouldn't forget to wake me. I showed it to him and I said, 'How do you like the picture?' and he sloughed it off.

"He said, 'hmmm, hmmm', and right then I realized, or was made to realize, that the picture was not as good as I thought it was. Because in effect my older brother had told me, 'It's not good because you're just a little kid. And you can't draw it as well as I can, because I'm older.' And ever since then, I think, if there's a rubber band, that's it.

"I've had a tendency to view myself as one who hasn't reached his prime yet, and I suppose, if I kept doing that, never would. Therefore, since I hadn't reached my prime, I wasn't as good as other people. And that would affect my potency in my expression, both oral and written, and film. Now I've rejected the equation that since I'm not as old as my brother I'm not as good as anybody else. I made that decision, that I wasn't as good as anybody else way back then, I think. And I've redecided that it's bull shit. I'm still going to be learning more, but what I know now for my age is fine.

"I'm doing a film this summer, which will be my most complicated. It involves sound, and we're filming it in the Pacific. There are just hundreds of details to get done before we go. I've been expanding my technical knowledge by doing test films. I've got to learn all about sound. The film this summer will be my first presentable effort since the marathon.

"I've gotten into college. Since I won't be around here as much, I've stayed close to the family. I'll be at the Art Institute, taking film making as a major. I hope they give me what I'm looking for. If they don't at least I'll be able to transfer with the good grades I can get there. Oh, and I won that same festival for the third time.

"I still love grass. I have a wonderful time on it; but I don't have to have it. I'm not saying anymore 'to have a groovy time you have to have it.' So that I can groove without grass, or with it. Because my head's OK as it is now. [*Hearty laugh.*] I feel a lot more OK than I thought I was. And more confident in myself. And I feel better now when I'm with other people.

"I'm especially glad I clarified those messages I got from my brothers. Because for two years at that school in the East I was my second brother's little brother. I was never really me. Except to the teachers who didn't like me. I knew that they didn't like *me* (ha, ha). I bought the message that since I'm not like him, what's the use? But I've gotten rid of both messages: number one, 'You're not even capable to begin with'; and the second one, 'You're not me, and you're not capable of becoming as good as me, so why don't you stay where you are?'

"The best effect from the marathon was 'hearing,' and junking those two messages."

9 Monitoring of Suicidal Risk

—Robert C. Drye[1], R.L.G., and M.M.G.

The authors describe a simple, rapid method by which patients with any suicidal ideas can determine for themselves and the evaluator what risk actually exists. The patient states how long he is willing to stay alive, without qualification, in the form of a decision rather than a promise or agreement with the evaluator. This method has been used successfully in various settings and with seriously ill patients.

In this paper we describe a method to be used by anyone evaluating a patient as a suicidal risk; the method enables the evaluator to make the following judgments: Is suicide a risk at all for this patient? If it is a risk, to what degree and for how long can the patient be trusted not to kill himself?

This second judgment is important at every stage of treatment in any setting, since on the basis of this judg-

First appeared in somewhat different form as "No-Suicide Decisions: Patient Monitoring of Suicidal Risk," in the *American Journal of Psychiatry*, 1973, *130*(2), 171-174. Used by permission of the American Psychiatric Association.

[1]Dr. Drye is a private practitioner in Seaside, California, a lecturer in psychiatry at Stanford University School of Medicine, a member of the faculty of the Western Institute, and a teaching member of the International Transactional Analysis Association.

ment the evaluator or therapist (and the patient) will decide on outpatient versus hospital care, and may decide to use the milieu, drugs, shock treatment, or psychotherapy in very different ways. (We have not used shock treatment with any patient evaluated under our method.)

Up to the present time no precise technique of measuring suicidal risk has been available to the evaluator. Various methods have been suggested for making the first judgment, including demographic and sociologic (Tuckman & Youngman, 1968; DeVos, 1968), psychodynamic, clinical historical, and interpersonal (Harris & Myers, 1968; Buglass & McCulloch, 1970; Fawcett et al., 1969), and biochemical (Bunney et al., 1969) criteria. Longitudinal studies of major mental illnesses have indicated higher risk for suicide among recovering depressed and schizophrenic patients (Roth, 1970). A classification of suicidal styles (Shneidman, 1968) has also been suggested. Shein and Stone (1969) have emphasized the importance of asking the patient directly about any suicidal thoughts—something that is not done often enough.

We believe that these approaches, which sometimes include rating scales and checklists, are useful in three ways. They increase the probability that evaluators will make some judgment about suicide; they help them in deciding that some risk does exist; and they may suggest preventive techniques at a large group or community level. However, they do not help evaluators enough with the second decision. On at least one scale (Tuckman & Youngman, ibid.), 35 percent of a group of high-risk patients actually committed suicide within a one-year follow-up (major attempts included). Such a high risk means that the evaluator must either excessively hospitalize patients or trust them not to commit suicide, while not knowing what degree of risk exists for a particular patient.

Evaluative comments such as "points toward" are not

precise enough in describing suicidal risk. They are likely to produce great anxiety in the patient, the evaluator, and concerned others. The therapist, who may be appealed to by a less experienced or less professional evaluator, does not necessarily have more confidence. Aphorisms such as, "You don't get paid for being smart. You get paid for sitting with this kind of patient"; or "You won't be a real psychiatrist until you've lost one," which we remember from our training days, are neither comfortable nor useful with the individual patient. Many suicidal patients invite the evaluator to overestimate or underestimate the risk by dramatic or demanding behavior.

We believe that our method offers substantial advantages both for accuracy in planning with the patient and in removing the burden on the evaluator. We share the evaluation tasks with the patients. Since they are the ones who are making the decision to kill themselves or not, they have the best data—not only on how intense the urge is, but on how strong the personal controls are. Specifically, patients can tell the evaluator how long, and under what conditions, they trust themselves to exercise control over their impulses. This approach developed out of our belief that the only therapeutic contracts likely to lead to change are those developed by the patients themselves, for which they will assume responsibility. Particular therapeutic schools that emphasize this approach and that have influenced us include psychoanalysis, transactional analysis, and gestalt therapy. The only exceptions to this approach would be with those patients who have organically impaired cerebral function. Psychotic patients who are willing to use this method can do so. The method will also work in any setting, including over the telephone, although there the evaluator's lack of awareness of the patient's body language may hinder evaluation.

Method

We suspect that suicidal fantasies may be present in any depressed patient, and in many patients with hypertension, a history of coronary occlusion, and other life-threatening illnesses. We investigate inappropriate laughter occurring during discussions of bad predictions (such as divorce, business failure, or illness). As part of history taking we often ask, "If things go badly for you, what will your life be like a year from now?" These are items developed from a checklist by Steiner (1967), and by McCormick (1971), to put patients in touch with the many important predictions they make for themselves, often outside of their awareness. If any suicidal or self-destructive fantasies appear, they are carefully investigated with the patient. These include fantasies of accidents, abuse of food, alcohol, or drugs, or exhausting work habits.

As soon as we believe that patients are aware of their fantasies, we ask them to make this statement: "No matter what happens, I will not kill myself, accidently or on purpose, at any time," and to report their internal responses to this statement. If the patient reports a feeling of confidence in this statement, with no direct or indirect qualifications, and with no incongruous voice tones or body motions, the evaluator may dismiss suicide as a management problem. In addition, the patient will often express considerable relief, since suicidal fantasies can be quite frightening. Finally, the settling of these fantasies frees patients who are not actively suicidal from ruminations they have been using to delay dealing with other reality or interpersonal or intrapsychic problems, since "If I'm going to commit suicide one of these days anyhow, why bother?"

The patient for whom suicide is an important issue will either object to or qualify the statement about suicide.

Objections are classified as "I can't" or "I won't." Patients who will not make the statement are assumed to be suicidal and they are advised that their choice is to make the statement with whatever qualifications they wish, or have us make arrangements for their security. If they say "I can't," we ask them to say "I won't," and to report whether this is closer to what they are feeling. (Whether or not they feel they can control their suicidal impulses, they are obviously *able* to make such a statement.) If they change to "I won't," we offer the choice between a statement and security arrangements, as before. At this point the evaluator can classify any patient as representing no risk, a very high risk, or a qualified risk.

Qualifications are classified as "until," "maybe," and "unless."

Until. The easiest qualification is time. While any time shorter than "never" allows for suicidal fantasy, we can plan very differently with a six-month safety margin than we can with an hour. A six-month span offers time for detailed therapeutic work on whatever reality or personal problem emerges elsewhere in the patient's qualifications. One hour allows the patient to make short moves unescorted, such as from our office to a nearby psychiatric ward. Furthermore, as patients experience even brief mastery of their suicidal impulses and begin to see possible solutions to their dilemma, they will usually fairly quickly extend the time qualification. All decisions are renewed before their time expiration, regardless of any apparent clinical improvement in the patient.

Maybe. In dealing with patients using "maybe," we emphasize that a decision for life is possible, but only the patient decides. For instance, "Nothing will happen," is a much feebler statement than "I won't do anything." "I'll try," "I'd like to," and "I'll probably" are all countered with "But will you?" "I promise" is also shaky; like the statement in the previous sentence, it often has the flavor of a child being asked by a parent to do something that the child regards as too unpleasant or difficult. The child's response is intended to get the parent to stop asking and not as a commitment.

Evaluators who accept an "I'll try" statement are making the same mistake as parents who accept trying instead of doing without recognizing the difference. The patients' statements like "I promise" provide many opportunities for setting up the evaluator as someone who is supposed to be disappointed, and the patients set themselves up for rebellion, shame, and guilt. Any decision they make is not an agreement with the evaluator, but a self-contained choice. (This, of course, does not psychologically diminish the potential importance of the evaluator.) The "I" may be supported by shortening the time span, or the evaluator may choose to do some brief therapy around the statement, "It sure seems important for you to be scared [angry, impulsive, confused]," reminding the patient that he has control over himself there, too.

Unless. This qualification allows the patient to shift responsibility for a suicidal act to someone or something else. (It may also be related to important therapeutic issues, once suicide has been temporarily removed from the foreground.) This type of qualification may be as vague as the philosophy, "People should be allowed to dispose of their own lives their own way"; or as immediate as, "I don't like what you [evaluator] are doing." Common statements include, "As long as my husband [wife, child, lover] does [or doesn't] . . .," "Unless I get drunk [tired, upset]," "Unless work [school, marriage] goes better," or their only apparently positive variations, "I'm too attached to my children," or "I'm such a coward." The whole purpose of an unqualified statement as a decision is to get the patient past just these external sources of trouble. Even if these are dropped after a time limitation, we feed these qualifications back to patients so they can hear how they use others to increase bad possibilities for themselves.

We do not argue with philosophical patients; unless they are willing to make a decision they are going to be supervised like anyone else. One of us (R. L. G.) often asks such patients, "Will you consider that what you call free choice is really a decision you made years ago? It only seems to be your free choice now?" If they are willing to consider this possibility, we may do some work around their original decision, and then ask again for a no-suicide contract now. The patient is in charge of how drunk or upset he is going to be, and what options he will allow himself in his important life situations; the details of this will be central in therapy.

The evaluator also does not take responsibility. For instance, if the evaluator will realistically not be available for frequent phone calls, this is included in the decision; i.e., "Even if I can't get hold of you." In practice, the evaluator will get occasional telephone calls, but far fewer than if he follows the common recommendations to tell the suicidal patient "I'm always available." (If the patient wants to call and we are available, we don't deny it.)

We previously noted that we ask the patient to state, "I will not kill myself, accidentally or on purpose, at any time." "Accidentally" is intended to deal with those patients who are unaware that they are in a suicidal position and who have had automobile accidents or skiing accidents, or are parachutists, or in some other way are seriously endangering their lives by their activities. Not everyone who skis or parachutes is in a suicidal position, of course, but everyone who doesn't fasten his seat belt, drives dangerously, or hurts himself skiing may be, and the truth may be obvious once the question is put to the patient. The same may be true of patients with hypertension, or a history of coronary occlusions, who may become aware of the ways in which they are endangering their lives once they have made a full statement.

Results

We have used this method with patients of all diagnostic categories, in hospitals, clinics, private offices, and community agencies, and in two- or three-day marathons with patients throughout the country. We have presented this method to many mental health professionals locally and nationally at major meetings and teaching centers.

We have sent questionnaires to all our trainees regarding their results. Thus far 31 therapists have reported on 609 patients, 266 of whom they considered seriously suicidal. One patient killed herself outside the time period. Three patients died or made serious suicidal attempts within the time period. One patient who was assumed to have organic brain disease (epilepsy) made a serious attempt. Another patient died in an automobile accident. State police said she was driving at a normal speed and wrecked her car while avoiding a poorly marked mud slide. The third patient took a fatal overdose of sleeping pills while drinking heavily. The 31 therapists we surveyed reported 20 suicides or serious attempts in their practice when they had not used this method, in most cases before they were aware of it.

Discussion

This combined diagnostic and management technique is suitable for use by inexperienced nonprofessionals as well as by experienced professionals. There are two situations where its use requires considerable flexibility.

One of these is long-term therapy, where the method itself becomes a major issue in the relationship and needs to be dealt with as such. The other situation is with patients who have made suicide the central theme of their lives. An adolescent and a 35-year-old divorcee, for instance, both spent most of every day working away from or toward suicide. As of this writing, the adolescent, who has never hurt herself seriously, either on or off a decision, has withdrawn from treatment for six months, with no serious attempts; the divorcee has been briefly hospitalized several times. Both patients occasionally called the therapist or other help givers at times when they doubted that they could continue on a particular decision. With both of these patients, the emptiness of their lives without the excitement surrounding suicide and the importance of the therapist's reactions to the frequent decisions are important issues. Finally, this method is not safe with patients who use alcohol or other drugs heavily until they also decide to stop using these drugs destructively.

10   *The Training of Psychotherapists in Transactional Analysis*

— R.L.G. (Ed.[1]*)*

Because the Western Institute primarily trains therapists who are already practiced as psychiatrists, psychologists, social workers, or pastors we direct our attention in this paper to the training of experienced therapists, rather than people at the level of first-year graduate school. We teach a set of guidelines for starting a new group or a new family; guidelines we at one time thought everyone would know—but they don't.

Contracts: There are three kinds: administrative, therapeutic, and psychological. The *administrative* contract is extremely important. It is not only between patient and therapist, but also between the therapist and his environment outside the group—his superiors, supervisors, employees, and supervisees. The most important question

---

First appeared in somewhat different form in *Voices: The Art and Science of Psychotherapy*, Fall 1974, 29-34. Used by permission of the American Academy of Psychotherapists.

[1]This paper was edited from the tapes of two sessions with our faculty at the Western Institute. The first session was with Erv and Miriam Polster, John McNeel, Gene Kerfoot, Jim Heenan, Mary and me; the second was with some of the above, Bob Drye, Ruth and George McClendon, and George Thomson. Some material I added following the sessions. In general, it gives a fair statement of our training.

is "How can I get fired?" Knowing the answer to that one, I know how to avoid getting fired. If I am working in an agency whose director doesn't like gestalt-TA, then I had better ask him to change, or change my style, or change jobs. The contracts need to be explicit and clear, not ambiguous.

> I once worked as a ward psychiatrist on a maximum security ward. The director of the hospital had several orders on several charts, restricting the patients' mobility. The first morning I went to him and asked him to cancel his orders. At first he refused. I asked him who was running my ward. He said I was. I told him to cancel his orders. He refused. I said I was going back to Carmel. He cancelled his orders. He called me a chowderhead. I said he could bawl me out all he wished, but he was to write no orders on my patients.

Therapeutic contracts—what the patient is changing about himself. Many therapists work without a specific therapeutic contract. It is very difficult for patients to know when they have arrived if they don't know where they are going. We teach our trainees to make specific, short-term contracts. Long-term contracts are OK too, of course, but often I want to know where someone is going *within* that long-term contract, a day at a time. In addition, I teach therapists when to *stop*. Even very good therapists don't always know when to quit. They go on and on and on, beyond where anything is going to happen. We teach four specific times to stop working: (1) *At the contracted time.* If I work from 9-12 and 2-5 and 7:30 to 9, as I usually do, then I stop at 12, 5 and 9, not 12:09, 5:15 or 9:30. No one plays "one more question, teacher" with me. (2) *At the point of a victory,* whether it is two minutes, or thirty minutes. Once an impasse has been bridged and the patient feels victorious, quit while ahead and let him enjoy the feelings. Let him get stroked. Too often I hear inexperienced therapists going for "just one more thing" until the patient is into another impasse and never has a chance to enjoy his victory. These are the therapists whose mothers said, "Be perfect!" (3) *At a solid impasse* I generally stop and let the patient feel the impact of the impasse. That is, if the work we do doesn't get through an impasse within a reasonable framework, I am willing to stop for now, rather than get into what Simkin calls a "bear trap." (4) *Within 30 minutes.* I teach my trainees to do a piece of work in 20 minutes, so that they learn how to listen for the first con, and the rest of the cons. I almost never work beyond 30 minutes with one patient. (Of course, if the therapist is doing all process work, then this or the other guides above are meaningless.)

The point of all the above is to keep therapy crisp, fruitful and fun, and to keep out of as many games as possible. All of us are going to get into some, but some reasonable guides like these do help to keep us out of most therapist-patient games. Most important is to teach therapists to be therapists, not *the rapist*. That is, many therapists don't know that it is vital to ask whether the patient is willing to go along the direction that the therapist wants to go. So often I have seen therapists do a piece of gestalt work without ever getting permission from the patient to work, so the patient goes along, reluctantly, being fucked over.

The *psychological contract* requires knowing what the patient is going to do, if left alone, to thwart the therapeutic contract. How is he going to con the therapist and con himself? Most of the guidelines I'm describing relate to the ways in which the therapist can keep the patient from fulfilling that psychological contract. In those of us who want to keep things as they are, the Adapted Child is almost always peeking around the corner saying, "I can't," "I wish," "I hope," "Perhaps," "If only," and other cop-out words.

Another simple set of guidelines is the *who, when, where, what, how* set. If the therapist follows this set, then there is more chance of therapy taking place, not just pastimes. *Who* refers to the transactions; if the patient is kept in the I-Thou, direct transactions either with other patients or with the therapist, or in relating a past event, more is likely to happen. For instance, a story of what someone's spouse did yesterday seldom gets anywhere. Usually when the patient tells the spouse in person or in fantasy what he said or did, movement begins, and affect is worked through. Talking about one's spouse who is in the room (indirect transaction) may lead to courtroom games and schizophrenia. The *when* and *where* are obvious—if everything that happens in the therapy room is in the here and now, then more work gets done. I don't mean by that that the patient can't deal with material outside the room; I mean that if he has something to bring in from the past and from somewhere else, then he acts as if the scene is happening in the here and now. *What* relates to what is being said. If what is being said interests all, more happens than if it interests only the patient. Patients in a group fall asleep when other patients tell long stories. Patients fall asleep if the therapist works beyond a reasonable time with one patient. *How* relates to meaningful, appropriate affect. Feelings inappropriate to what is happening are nontherapeutic. The therapist must either go where the patient is, or get the patient back to where the others are. For example, hebephrenic giggling doesn't get anyone anywhere.

The best way we know to get these guidelines, and everything else important, across to the trainees is to treat our trainees ourselves. Most residency programs, most PhD and MSW programs that I know of do not; most of them don't even require the student to be in treatment. I was the chairman of a panel at AGPA, several years ago, on the supervision of experienced group therapists. No one on the panel, no one in the audience, treated the trainees except me. I don't see how we can train properly if we don't treat as part of the training contract.

Jim Heenan: The analytic schools do.

Bob Goulding: No, one analyst trains a student, and another does the analysis. I don't want to criticize another model but to talk about what *we* do that is different. The issue is, if a therapist in training is a hard "Kick Me" player who is depressed and in a suicidal script, it is important that he be in touch with his game, and that the supervisor pick up the game as the trainee plays it with his cotrainees. Then in the therapy session, the supervisor can explore the injunctions, decisions, games and script, and facilitate the trainee's getting well. If he doesn't, the trainee gets through his training, is still depressed, and doesn't deal well with other people who play "Kick Me" and are depressed and suicidal.

Erv Polster: There is still another part of it: learning by immediate experience. Not only do you get a person to the position where he is cured, but he knows the process, having been a party to it.

Mary Goulding: We are very aware of the people who do not allow themselves to be treated. Often these are the people who don't pay their own way to the workshop, whose agencies send them; who don't get involved in their own treatment, and who are not gifted treaters. They are frightened of treatment themselves and don't have that experience you spoke of, Erv. They do all kinds of things to keep their patients from having therapeutic experiences.

Gene Kerfoot: The neat thing I see about how we do it is that while being a therapist in the group, the trainee can see how he gets into his racket—frustration, for example—and two minutes later be the patient, with a peer or one of us treating him, working with him on how he got *into* his frustration, and how he can get *out*.

Miriam Polster: An attractive thing to me is that this does away with the snobbery of who is patient, who is therapist.

Jim Heenan: And that the therapist in training, who is working with one of his peers, can get in touch with something, negotiate with his patient to stop at that moment, and perhaps reverse roles.

John NcNeel: I think it is important that the supervision go on while the trainee is doing the leading. One of the things that happens is that they find out the subtle ways in which they fall into other people's behavior patterns, for instance that they become Mother or Father for the client; very subtle ways that are hard for them to see or feel. When the objective trainer is sitting right there, watching them, he can come in and show them, at that moment, how they have fallen into the client's trap, and of course their own trap. This is not something you can do with tapes later, or in memory recall later, because the subtlety gets lost. And you don't get to it by talking *about* it later.

Bob Goulding: Yeah, the best place to deal with countertransference is at the moment it occurs in the group. I'm glad you brought that up, John, because I can remember, in my residency training, I remembered what I wanted to remember. Even with all my tape supervision with Eric [Berne], weekly for two years, we couldn't get to the things we all get to with live supervision.

Mary Goulding: I'd like to move to another subject, the place of stroking in training. Most teaching in the school system is not good teaching because the teachers spend their time pointing out errors rather than victories. Teachers say, "You spelled this word wrong," rather than "You spelled 1,241 words right, hooray!" The same principle applies to psychotherapy. We build on whatever strength the trainee therapist comes with, and give positive stroking for the good things he does. If he does something flagrantly bad, I'll simply stop and show him other alternatives.

Miriam Polster: I go along with that, Mary. I also like to point out specific talents that my trainees have. For example, somebody this morning had a really good ear for language, he was able to use words in a new way and move the therapy along.

Erv Polster: I like to supervise that way, too, but let me put in a plug for unsupervised practice. In our gestalt programs, we have both. We break into triads and some people work alone, without supervision, others with us. The idea of leading the practice without anyone looking on is an invaluable thing to be able to do. There is a leader, a worker, and an observer.

Mary Goulding: What do you do with someone who is too scared, too sick, too concrete to ever be a good therapist?

Erv Polster: In our program in Cleveland hardly anyone failed to get through. In a three-year program, if you noticed they weren't ready for the third year, they could take the second year over. We made certain recommendations for them and finally they would get through. It is easier to do that in a post-post graduate institute than it is in graduate school. In graduate school it is hard to transcend the students seeing the teachers as evaluators, not teachers.

Miriam Polster: Also there is another process. The people who think they might not finish don't start, they select themselves out.

Bob Goulding: We just had a psychiatrist decide after one week of a four-week workshop that he didn't even want to be a physician anymore, and he went home! Sometimes the problems we have are a little different. A year or two ago we had a psychiatrist who was a terrible therapist, who was harmful to people. We wouldn't let him do a minithon with community patients; that was then a part of the training. He was furious and said, "I've been treating patients for 20 years." I said, "I don't give a damn, you are not treating ours." He is still treating patients, however, and telling everyone he was trained by us. What the hell can we do?

Erv Polster: Yeah, that's one of the prices we pay for a certain looseness in certification, but the price is low compared to the value of an open community. And this guy was already a therapist.

Bob: I would call him *the rapist* rather than therapist.

Miriam Polster: This brings up the selection process, which I haven't resolved for myself yet. How do you know when a guy is a late bloomer, who doesn't meet your selection procedure, but might be very talented?

Mary Goulding: Some who don't have the credentials do get by sometimes, and sometimes they are very good—and sometimes they are horrid.

Bob Goulding: Our application blank helps screen out unqualified people because those who really are not going to make it don't have the nerve to apply. Ordinarily, for a four-week workshop we won't take applicants who have been hospitalized. But we will accept them for a three-day workshop first, as a screening procedure. However, we have had some pretty crazy psychiatrists, whom we have just sent home after a few days. The intense pace is too much for someone who is that loose.

Jim Heenan: We have another selection procedure you haven't mentioned—those that can take off a month, pay the tuition and the air fare, are already winners!

Gene Kerfoot: The whole business of practice groups I thought was super when I was training here, because they take the magic out of therapy; when you are treated by, and 30 minutes later you treat, a peer.

Bob Goulding: Wasn't it you who was a trainee when I worked on and cured my headache?

Gene Kerfoot: Yeah.

Bob Goulding: Great job—haven't had one since. Great therapist.

Erv Polster: What about reading?

Bob Goulding: We discussed this for some time. All of us ask trainees to read; but without a grade system, without a diploma of some kind, there's no way we can get everyone to read. The reading most of us require includes Perls, Berne, the Polsters, Freud, Goulding, and the Sager-Kaplan *Progress in Group and Family Therapy*. We also discussed the ongoing lectures in psychopathology that everyone must have. We then discussed homework and what the therapist can do away from the training to improve his skills.

Gene Kerfoot: One thing we haven't talked about, Bob, is what you did with Eric, and what you insist we all do; that is, listen to your own tapes, or watch and listen to video tapes.

Bob Goulding: Eric taught me to listen at least six times. Listen to me and my ego state changes, the patient and his/her ego state changes, the patient's games, and whether I hooked into responding to his games. I also teach people to listen to the first con, which they probably missed when it was offered, and to all the cop-out words they use—therapist and patient—like "will you *try* to do so and so," rather than "will you *do* so and so." I'll attribute 25 percent of my skill to that listening I did 15 years ago.

Mary Goulding: You're the most fantastic listener I know; you almost never miss anything.

John McNeel: One of the advantages of supervising ongoing groups by mail is that the therapist has to listen to his own tape in order to select out what he wants me to hear, and he has to listen to hear what I say later.

Jim Heenan: Another thing we do that I never learned before, that is a major difference between our training and that given in universities, is the stress on contracts. I think one of the main reasons our success rate is so high is that we negotiate workable contracts, and we teach people how to do it. Most therapists that we train have never been taught that before.

Miriam Polster: I ask people to tell me what they add to therapy, and what they take away.

Erv Polster: I teach them how to transcend professionalism. It's very hard to teach without getting across that there is *the* way to do it, even though you don't intend to do that. I try to teach them that what they do is based on what they have learned, rather than their having become a mechanized version of the teacher.

Mary Goulding: Some people learn first by copying, though, and that's all right. We taught some therapists in a foreign country gestalt techniques for two days, then watched them use them for two hours with a live group, even though they didn't always fit. By using, they learn.

George Thomson: One of the things that we do is let people work with their own styles, from the very first day of training. How long was I in school before I could do a group? Therapy is learned by doing therapy, not by listening to it being done or reading about it.

Jim Heenan: And we teach them to supervise from the first day, like in the fishbowl experience. Here we use Bob's model, where each trainee is assigned something to watch for in a small group. There might be a leader, four "patients," and 15 observers; with one looking for ego state changes, another listening for games, another watching for incongruent body movements, and so forth.

Bob Drye talked about presenting, after the therapy sessions, didactic material that fits what happened that day, about the development of new theory in seminars, where trainees are encouraged to theorize—what is the trainee going to do with his training? This is essential for trainers like Irv Kraft in Houston, Harris Peck in New York, and Graham Barnes in Chapel Hill, who also are training nonprofessionals to do specific things, as group treaters in hospital settings, youngsters in drug drop-in centers, etc.

Bob Goulding: Bob, you weren't at the first session, what do you do about bad therapists?

Bob Drye: Well what I do—what I learned from you in the first place, at AGPA before I joined you, is that you guys have the only clear idea of what to do about that problem; and that is to treat him. The previous cleanest work was a research project about five years ago or so that indicated that at least half the therapists in the country, including psychoanalysts, are doing lousy work.

Bob Goulding: That's a very conservative estimate!

Bob Drye: Well most places *think* they are getting rid of the worst, rather than dealing with them, but they don't get rid of all the worst! We treat them, and treat them until they are good.

Mary Goulding: A small part of the problem may be inferior students.

Bob Drye: The problem is inferior students, inferior faculty, and inferior tools. As a psychoanalyst, I can say clearly that the psychoanalytic model is a lousy model for teaching psychotherapy. I believe that it is important for teachers to have effective tools, so they can teach and know what to do when they are not teaching effectively. You guys have those tools; that's why I am here.

Bob Goulding: In closing, I want to say one more thing. I think the most important item that I teach is for therapists and everyone to stay in the here and now. There is no way for me to feel bad, ordinarily, if I stay in the immediate now. There is no way for me to be anxious about tomorrow if I am paying attention to today. If I must look ahead, then I can look ahead with enthusiasm about what each new day brings. And if the immediate now is bad, then I had better get the hell out of this here and now and find another here that's better.

11   Client Impasses in TA
       Treatment   —R.L.G.

All client impasses seen in therapy appear to relate to archaic impasses, and, when viewed from a transactional analysis perspective, they seem to be of three specific kinds.

The first, which I call a first-degree impasse (see figure 1, p. 80) derives from what TA theorists call the counterinjunction, the message from the Parent ego state of the parent. It is usually what the parent asks the child to do so that the parent can be proud of her or him, as "Work hard so that you can get into medical school (so I won't be totally sorry you were born"). We see this in many of the therapists we train who are still working hard, not enjoying, at 30, 40, 50 years of age. This is one of the impasses that many encounter leaders deal with in their general "experiments." Working with this impasse is fairly simple. It is between the Parent ego state and the Child ego state, and is resolved by a simple dialogue between Child and Parent, with the Adult making the decision; e.g., to knock off working so hard. The client then allows himself to work only 50 hours instead of 70 or 80,

This article first appeared in somewhat different form, as "Thinking and Feeling in Transactional Analysis: Three Impasses," in *Voices: The Art and Science of Psychotherapy*, Spring 1974, 11-13. Used by permission of the American Academy of Psychotherapists.

and starts playing golf or tennis or going fishing more often. However, he may then find himself working very hard at golf, or trying to catch all the fish in Yellowstone Park.

We then run into the second-degree impasse, which is originally between the Child ego state of the parent and the Child ego state of the client. It is introjected in the Child ego state by the client (see figure 2, p. 82).

This is usually a far earlier message than that in the first illustration, and, in a case like this one, may well be, "Don't exist," heard in such statements as, "If you hadn't come along I wouldn't have had to marry your no-good father," or, "I could have been an opera singer," or, "My troubles are all your fault." As long as the client is working hard, listening to the counterinjunction, he can avoid listening to the injunction not to exist; when he stops working hard, a little voice in his head may say, "If you're not working hard, you might as well not be here," and he begins to get depressed. (This is the danger of working through the first-degree impasse in an encounter session, if the leader doesn't know enough to recognize the danger of letting the client go home without some deeper awarenesses; e.g., that the encounterer depresses himself when he is not getting strokes for working so hard and may end up driving off a cliff on the way home from the session.) In a dialogue between his introjected Child of his parent and his own little Adult (called the Little Professor, that part of us that may make a decision to ignore the injunction in order to survive in a hostile environment as a child), he may then be able to say, in an affective manner, "I am not listening to you. I am not going to die, or kill myself, to please you." In working with this impasse the therapist usually encourages some regression, asking the client to remember earlier and earlier scenes, until he fantasies a real scene of childhood when he first decided it might be easier to die than to tolerate his environment (since his not existing is what will please mother anyhow). In this relived scene, he experiences the feelings he did in the original scene, so that his new decision, to exist, comes from his Child ego state, with tremendous affective relief.

The third-degree impasse is between the Adapted Child and the Free or Natural Child (see figure 3, p. 83). I don't know how to draw a structural diagram to illustrate this impasse, and have changed the diagram of the Child into the functional one seen here. (The Adapted Child may be further divided by showing positive adaptation and rebellious adaptation.) Here the injunction not to exist is so early, perhaps even prenatal, that the person feels not worthwhile, valueless, and deserving death. A recent example of this kind of work was done with a dream in which the client thought he had a cancer that was killing him. As he took the part of the cancer, he felt himself being the killing agent, and as the dialogue developed, he claimed both parts. He then overcame the killing part of himself—saying as his Free Child, "I am not going to let me kill me," and as his Adapted Child, "I am feeling weaker and weaker," first with rage at himself, and finally with laughter, as he broke through the impasse.

Knowledge of these three degrees of impasses will help the therapist in creating with the client an environment for change, and will help the client to understand his treatment after the gestalt work is done. We have found, as did Lieberman, Yalom, and Miles (1973) in their work with "encounter" groups, that the therapist who provides cognitive structure, who stimulates affective experience moderately, who cares, and who is moderately directive in his work, gets the highest gain. Such cognitive structure as the script matrix, together with the drawing of the level of the impasse, is important for the patient, after he works through his affective experience, in consolidating his gains.

12   *Curing Phobias*   —R.L.G.

During the past four years we have been developing a TA-based theory of phobias. At first we thought that a phobia was always a defense against an injunction-decision complex, because we saw many phobias of high places, water, elevators, etc., that were directly related to a fear of dying. To us it was logical that if a fear of dying was present, there must have been, at one time, a threat to life. One threat to life is the injunction, given to some in early childhood, "Don't exist." The child's Adult thinks, "This is pretty scary, so I had better stay away from scary places," and then doesn't go near any threatening situation, like on a high building, or near the water, because he might fall, jump, or get thrown. As he grows, the original threat is forgotten and he maintains the displacement. Once he decides that he is never going to kill himself, in any way, including jumping off a building, he then doesn't need the phobia to protect him, and he gives it up, perhaps spontaneously.

But early we became aware that sometimes he also used his phobia to maintain the injunction-decision as well. For instance, one patient who was phobic of high places, airplanes, and going out by himself, had as a child made the decision, "If things get too bad I'll kill myself or run away." When he was in his Child ego state and

First appeared in somewhat different form in *Voices: The Art and Science of Psychotherapy*, Spring 1975,30-31. Used by permission of the American Academy of Psychotherapists.

having a dialogue with his fantasied mother, he was asked
to tell her, "I will never kill myself or run away." He replied, "No, I won't tell her that, because if things get
much worse, if my phobia gets worse, I *will* kill myself."
However, his phobia kept him from doing so, because he
would not leave his house or his office or anywhere without someone with him. His original statement to us was,
"I *can't* go out by myself." Always having someone with
him made it much more difficult for him either to run
away or kill himself.

When he finally redecided that he would never kill
himself, and then had in fantasy a desensitization trip of
going out by himself, he immediately went out of the
workshop and walked around the block in a large city by
himself—and went out by himself thereafter. At the same
time he gave up his lifelong depression. However, he was
still phobic of planes, although he did take one trip in a
chartered plane.

The maintenance of this one phobia, which we did not
treat after the first desensitization, was probably on another level. Instead of protecting him from the injunction,
this phobia seemed to maintain the injunction-decision—
but this was *another* injunction, *another* decision, different from the "Don't exist" injunction, and the decision
that some day if things got too bad he would kill himself.
Here the fear of planes kept him from being totally successful in his business—in order for him to be the top
man, he had to fly all over the world. If he *wouldn't* fly
(he said he *couldn't* fly) then he would never be elected
president of his company. Here the injunction and the
decision were quite clear: The injunction from his father
and his mother was, "You'll never make it [Don't make
it]" His decision was, "No matter how hard I try, I'll
never make it." Originally this had to do with not getting
approval from his mother for any good deed, and for get-

ting his father to intercede. The only way his father would intercede was for him to be so sick, so depressed, that father would take pity on him. Later he got support for not making it from his brothers who rode him hard whenever he made a bad business decision, until he get depressed; then the oldest brother intervened.

Thus, in this case the phobia maintained the early injunction-decision complex.

Another illustration: The patient, a skillful therapist, said, at the end of my lecture on phobias that she would like me to do a demonstration with her fear of fast cars, motorboats, roller coasters, etc. We ran through a number of examples in the here and now, looking for some early fears, and got back to a series of scenes when, as Mother, she said to herself, "Don't do anything that you might get hurt doing." (The injunction here was "Don't.") In these scenes Mother told her to be scared because of Mother's own scare. I was sure that the injunction "Don't" was designed by Mother's Child ego state to protect Mother from her own Parent, because of Mother's early desire for the nonexistence of the pregnancy, and her own feelings of guilt around that desire. The only way Mother could then protect herself from the Punitive Parent was to overprotect the child by not letting her do *anything* that might have ended in the child's harm or death. Thus, in a way, she episcripted (English, 1969) the child in order to get rid of her own fear and anxiety. At any rate, in the work we did the patient responded spontaneously to her Mother (her own P_1) with, "Hey, I'm not buying your scare anymore. I am not going to be scared. I am not afraid of situations where I know there is no real danger. I won't, I *am not* listening anymore." The dialogue went on for a while, and then she turned to me and said, "I'd like to do so some desensitization." I then led her through a short fantasy of riding in a fast motorboat while her husband, and then her son, water skied—a terrifying situation for her in the past. She then said, "I am feeling excited rather than scared, and I would like to go ride a roller coaster." The whole group then drove to Santa Cruz and she went on roller coasters, and other previously terrifying rides, with great excitement, no fear, phobia, or anxiety.

With patients who are afraid of bugs, snakes, cockroaches, worms, etc., we were not able to isolate the original injunction-decision complex that related to the phobia. In these cases, our hunch was that whatever the child impasse was, the patient had since dealt with dealt with it, and the phobia of these insects and reptiles was a displacement that had lost connections. In these cases, if the patient wanted to give up the phobia (and many did not) we simply entered into a short desensitization. In one case of a phobia of cockroaches,[1] in fantasy we marched in one cockroach, bringing him closer and closer, then moving him out, then back, until the patient finally broke out laughing, and said, "Hell, I'm not afraid of cockroaches any longer." We then marched in a whole platoon, then a whole army of cockroaches until she laughed again, got out of her chair, picked up an imaginary broom, and swept the roaches out.

Thus we have found several decisions that seem to have produced a phobic response—the defense against an injunction-decision or the maintenance of an injunction-decision. In many cases the patient gives up the phobia spontaneously with a redecision. In other cases one, occasionally two, desensitizations are helpful. In all cases, the patient is asked, as soon as possible, to go out and do the things he was afraid of doing; climbing a mountain,

---

[1]This is a different case from the one Mary writes about in chapter 17.

going up in a tall building, riding an elevator, swimming, or riding roller coasters. There have been no failures to date except the above-mentioned man who would still not fly. We would like to have treated him by having him get in touch with the "Don't make it" injunction, but perhaps his Little Professor was right. Perhaps he would never have made a good president.[2]

---

[2] I have since seen the patient who used his phobia of flying to keep himself from becoming president of his company. During the interview I asked him to take both sides of the impasse regarding flying: the side that wouldn't fly, and that used his fear to keep himself from flying, and the part of him that wanted to fly, to be free. In the work he recognized that he was using his phobia to keep from being important, from being president. He then realized that he didn't *want* to be president, and that all he wanted was to live out his life doing a job less than president, and enjoying himself.

At the conclusion of the work he decided that he didn't have to be afraid in order not to fly; that he could either not fly or fly for fun; and that he didn't have to become president if he flew.

With this decision he was willing to take a short flight, which he joyfully reported to us. Later he wrote with great enthusiasm that he had flown on a short commercial run and had had a great time doing so, and that he was looking forward to flying to the United States to see us, and to enjoy things he had been thinking about most of his life.

13 The Formation and Beginning Process of Transactional Analysis Groups
—R.L.G.

Transactional analysis (TA) began with Eric Berne (1961, 1977). In the mid-fifties, Eric noticed the uniformity of variabilities in a given person's behavior. For example, at one moment a girl would be curled up on the chair and behaving and sounding like a 5-year-old; at the next she would be sitting bolt-upright and shaking her finger and scolding; and next she would be giving information in a calm, grown-up manner. As he studied further, Eric noticed that this behavior repeated itself, and that when the girl behaved as a child, she would look similar to the way that she looked when she had previously behaved as a child. When she behaved as a scolding parent, she was also consistent in the way she looked and sounded, but this was entirely different behavior, different voice, different vocabulary, from the childlike behavior.

First appeared in somewhat different form in *Basic Approaches to Group Psychotherapy and Group Counseling*, G. M. Gazda (Ed.), 1975. Used by permission of Charles C. Thomas, Publisher, Springfield, Ill.

From this grew the awareness of sets of ego states—
that people have three different personalities—one that
they maintain from an earlier time, one that they copy
from their real parents and parent surrogates, and one
that fits their chronological age. These three sets of ego
states Eric called the Parent, the Adult, and the Child.

In the early days, most of the talk and meetings around
these interesting observations were held at Eric's office
in San Francisco, or at his home in Carmel, California.
He shared them at poker games with me and other
friends, and he shared them with Barbara Rosenfeld and
David Kupfer and other professionals in Carmel. Later,
in his San Francisco office, he started the Social Psychiatry Seminars (SFSPS). During these early days, in the late
fifties and early sixties, the seminars were attended by
Mel Boyce, Joe Concannon, Frank Ernst, Ken Everts, Vi
Litt, Frances Matson, Ray Poindexter, and Myra
Schapps. Barbara Rosenfeld went off to Philadelphia to
get her MD; Claude Steiner, who had been in the early
movement, was in Ann Arbor getting his PhD; Gordon
Haiberg and Tom Harris from Sacramento joined the
group; Paul McCormick and Bill Collins, corrections
workers, were also in the early seminars, which I joined
in January, 1962.

I mention those early days because it was there, in San
Francisco, that the theory of transactional analysis developed from the ideas of all of us. The early *Transactional
Analysis Bulletin* (now the *Transactional Analysis Journal*), first published in January, 1962, contained many
clinical notes from which the theory developed. Eric's
first book on TA, *Transactional Analysis in Psychotherapy*
(1961), described the development of the theory in detail,
and *Games People Play*, published in 1964, conveyed the

theory of games more completely. We had a difficult time getting *Games People Play* published, because the publishers were not willing to take the financial risk. Finally, Eric offered to pay them $3,000 for the first edition and a private printing of 1,000 copies. He persuaded all of us (about 30) to buy 30 copies each—at regular cost. We agreed, and the first printing was done. As everybody knows, the book, to our surprise, became a tremendous best seller.

Selection and Group Composition

The concept of group therapy as practiced by most transactional analysts is quite different from the classical process group that I learned from psychoanalysts in Baltimore. In the first place, the very selection of patients for a group is different. I learned all kinds of principles about selection, in a Veteran's Administration clinic and hospital, that we totally disregard now; there is almost no patient criterion except that we have space in the group for him, and he agrees to come. I put all patients in groups, regardless of symptoms, classification of diagnosis, age, sex, marital status, or race. I have even had a man's mistress in the same group with him and his wife. All our groups are of two kinds: (1) open-end, ongoing groups, or (2) limited weekend, or week-long, or month-long groups. The ongoing groups operated by my associates are completely open-end, although a few transactional analysts have tried limited groups of 10 sessions, or three months, and the like.

My own groups, at this time, are primarily for professionals, and are all of the marathon type. Patients who

come to my marathons are all referred by other therapists, and they are mixed with the professionals. These
professionals might include, for example, a chairman of
a department of psychiatry, a leading psychoanalyst, and
a California Youth Authority counselor with a BA degree.
We see no objection at all to such a wide range of "patients." In 10 years we have had no difficulty with this
arrangement.

The type of group determines, to some degree, the selection process and the composition of the group. There
is a wide difference between the once-a-week, open-end
group and a marathon group. The open-end type is just
that. Patients have been coming and going for 10 years,
so there are no longer any "opening remarks," or the like.
Patients are generally seen individually at least once, but
in some cases more than once. Sometimes they call when
there is no time for a private interview, and then they are
put unceremoniously for that week into whatever group
has an opening.

Group Size

The average size of our ongoing groups is eight, although we do take up to 10, but no more than 10. Our
marathons are held to 14, although I prefer 12. Fourteen
is the number that is necessary to allow us to operate the
groups economically. Our one-week workshops are held
to 20, and our four-week workshops enroll a maximum
of 32.

Patient Contract

The first therapeutic move with any new patient is the contract. If the patient has been seen individually, he may already have worked out his contract. Even so he will do it again, since all of our groups are run by cotherapists. (This is not true of all TA groups, because Eric was against the use of cotherapists. But all of our groups operate with cotherapists, neither of whom is an assistant.) The contract is reached by carefully working out with the patient whatever it is he particularly wants to change. We need to be very careful to work for a contract goal that is set by the patient's Child or Adult ego state, and not his Parent. For instance, I did a three-day workshop for professionals. One of the professionals said that he wanted to gain better control of his anger. I was surprised at this, because I had known him for six years and I had never seen any evidence of his anger. Further questioning of this goal provided me information about his recent marriage. He was becoming angry at his stepchildren, who were somewhat disruptive. It was important for him to get in better touch with an anger that he had never before allowed himself, because of the old parental injunction: "Don't get angry!" This man spent so much energy "controlling his anger" that he had very little energy left for other feelings, and he was thought to be rather cold. When he did some work on anger, he was then able to begin to drop it, rather than to involve us in collusion with his early parents to "control" it.

The contract is extremely important, honored by all TA therapists whom I know, because through it we do two essential things: (1) We have a specific place from which to work, rather than sit around for 10 years allowing the patients to "process." (2) We have a point by which to measure success of treatment. If a patient states that he wants to "understand himself better," there is no way of measuring this, whereas if he states that he wants to stop feeling depressed, or get rid of his headaches, this can be measured.

Beginning a Group

In a new group, or marathon, we get contracts from everyone before any definitive work is done. It may take a half-day of a marathon. Here, however, there are some differences. We do not lecture to a new group, or to a new patient in a group, but we begin all our marathons with about three hours of theory before we start the contracting. This serves a number of purposes. Although the theory is presented for the benefit of the therapists, so that they are able to recognize the theoretical base of the practical work, we have learned that all do better work during the marathon if they have a theoretical structure. Lieberman, Yalom, and Mile's book, *Encounter Groups: First Facts* (1973), reported that patients given a "cognitive structure" were among those who improved the most. We give them permission to use their heads, whereas Fritz Perls and other gestaltists told their patients to lose their heads and come to their senses. We provide most patients with Campos and McCormick's *Introduce Yourself to TA* (1969), which is superb.

When describing the initial procedures in a TA group, I consider two quite different frameworks: (1) the classical, Berneian position, and (2) the Goulding tradition. Many therapists around the country who have been trained by me use my method, whereas most of the old San Francisco group use Eric's method.

Eric, after the contract was negotiated, did therapy in four steps. First, he analyzed ego states of the individiuals in the group; second, he analyzed transactions; third, he analyzed games; and fourth, he analyzed scripts. The script work was done with close attention given to the patient's early memory of favorite stories or fables that fit his life style, and to the people in the patient's life that fit the people in the story. This procedure is an analysis of displacement, and we usually do not do it.

Following the contract negotiations, we are more likely to start working with individual patients in the group concerning their racket. We define *racket* as the person's chronic bad feelings that usually lead to no action. Rackets, which are remnants of childhood, include such feelings as anger, depression, confusion, anxiety, and boredom. We never ask, "What makes you angry?" but rather, "What do you do to maintain your anger?" "What did you do last year?" "What did you get angry about in college? in high school? in grade school? before you went to school?" By this chronological regression we usually can reach an early memory of anger very easily. We do not just accept "telling about" an experience, but rather we get the patient to be in the scene, to tell it as if it were happening right now.

When we get to an early scene, we ask the patient to "act out" not only his response, but also the response of Mother, or Father, or sibling. We do this by setting up a two-chair dialogue in which we ask the patient to move back and forth between the two chairs. This, of course, is a gestalt technique; it is an excellent way to help the patient get some clear definitions of his ego state boundaries.

At this point, when we have professionals in the group, they begin to get restless and ask questions like, "We might as well not be here; don't you ever use the other people in the group?" Or they might become involved by asking, "How does that make you feel?" To this line of questioning, we cry "tilt." We are not inclined to sit back and listen to a group talk, but we are more inclined to work with one patient for a period of about 30 minutes.

The other transactions from the group members may be from their Adults, good straightforward confrontations; or they may be ostensibly Adult, but actually the first move in a game. If we see them as the former, we stroke for good work; if we see them as the first move in a game, we wait to see what develops. For instance, someone in the group may ask a patient who is working on his anger, "Have you ever tried Librium?" This sounds like the first move in a "Why Don't You—Yes But" game, and we would probably wait to see who else gets in, how the patient responds, and what feelings develop. If the patient's answer after every question is "Yes, but I . . .", we would probably stop the process after two or three transactions. Then we would ask the patient what he feels, and we would also ask the other group members who have been involved what it is that they feel. If the patient feels discouraged, or angry, and the others feel frustrated, we are sure they have been in a game. We then define the game, draw it on the blackboard, and point out to the patient how he uses the game to maintain his anger. We also tell the other group members how they use the game to maintain their frustration.

I referred to "tilt" earlier to call attention to the fact that many, if not most, individuals honestly believe that people can make other people angry, depressed, bored, confused, and anxious. One of the major propositions of TA, or at least our brand of TA, is that each person is responsible for his own feelings, and that he chooses to respond in a fairly stereotyped way, depending upon his own rackets, if the feelings are spurious.

Thus, when we hear a professional in a group ask another, "How does that [or he, or she] make you feel?" we immediately respond with our code word *tilt*—meaning that you have just made an illegal movement and the pinball game is over! For too long, parents have blackmailed their children by saying to them, "You make me so depressed when you get C's and D's on your report card," or "You give me a headache when you make all that noise." Therapists who do the same thing in groups accentuate this blackmail—implying that an individual is not responsible for his own feelings. We see the games people play as the means by which they maintain their feeling rackets.

Thus, in the first group session, we get contracts and we begin to teach people that they are autonomous and responsible, not only for their own actions, but also for their own feelings. This self-responsibility is extremely important from the very beginning. We call to the attention of our patients each of their words and gestures that denies responsibility for self. We respond to words like "can't," "try," "want," "wish," "hope," "perhaps," "would if," "if it weren't for," and many others. For patients who say, "I can't quit smoking," or, "I want to quit smoking," while puffing on a cigarette, we ask them to say, "I won't quit," and then have them get in touch with what they feel as they say it. Children are taught that they are not allowed to say "won't," but that it is all right for them to say "I can't," or "I'll try," or whatever response they can use that gets both parents and child off the hook. Most of these words, which we call cop-out words, are a result of internal Parent-Child conflicts that have not been resolved, and we see no possibility of resolving them until the patient claims his own power.

If we are doing a marathon, there is an entirely different tempo to working on the problem of autonomy from that used in an ongoing group, which is the reason why many TA therapists are now doing marathons, either as a regular function of an ongoing group or as a way of working certain patients through the impasse they are in. A patient having one and a half hours of group per week and then 166½ hours away from the group will probably not make as many changes as he will working for 20 hours over a weekend, where he can practice some of his newly discovered potency with others in the same position.

The first time we see a game being played, and someone picking up a payoff of bad feelings, we ask him first to become aware of those feelings, and then we ask him if he knows how he got there. For instance, in a practice group, the therapist was getting contracts from a five-member group, with other participants observing, and making notes of rackets, games, body movements, etc. Three people in the group, in a counterclockwise order, made contracts. Then the fifth started to work. The fourth waited until he was through, then turned to him angrily and said, "How come you didn't let me speak?" (Note the "let me speak.") "Are you angry?" asked the therapist. "Of course," she replied. He then diagrammed on the blackboard the way she had maneuvered herself into the position of feeling angry because he "didn't let her speak," although she had had the obvious option of speaking out immediately and stating that it was her turn. "But that wouldn't be polite," she said. And then the whole archeology of the game became obvious. In the service of her childhood anger, she allowed her Parent ego state to say to her, "Don't interrupt; it's not polite," which was obviously a rehash of an old family scene, repeated many times. She was still angry about all those times, and still played out the scene in many little ways.

There are several other points to make concerning this practice-group session, which lasted about 20 minutes, that illustrate well the course of a TA group. In 10 minutes the leader had heard four contract goals, picked up a racket that gave him clues to pick up a game, confronted the patient with the game, and in five minutes more had a contract from her to stop setting herself up for anger. This doesn't mean, of course, that she would never "play" again. The next time she played (about 15 minutes later), she started to become angry, and then suddenly howled with laughter and said, "I did it again, didn't I?" and dropped her anger. Such a recognition, in her "guts," that she had played a game, permitted her to replace the anger with genuine enjoyment of something she had learned for herself.

Very early in our TA groups, we pick up the principal rackets, the principal games, and how these rackets and games fit a lifelong style, or "script." It is the theory in TA that most, if not all of us, live out our lives in some kind of a self-defeating script, which may be "heroic" or may be "banal." In the heroic script, the protagonist may go down fighting the Holy Crusades, such as by being disbarred, being carried off the field on the shields of his friends, becoming bankrupt or penniless, or by killing himself. In the banal script, he lives out a life without a great deal of excitement and without a great deal of joy.

To illustrate a script being played, I'll refer to another 20-minute, group-practice session. One of the professionals stated that his contract goal was to "stop not asking his own patients for contracts." He said also that he led several groups, and that somehow he failed to make clear contracts with most of the patients in the groups. As a result, he then felt inadequate, incompetent, and sometimes depressed, and thought about quitting psychiatry—maybe running away, perhaps killing himself. The leader quickly moved into the frequency with which the patient had had these feelings in the past, moved back into a childhood scene in which the patient remembered that he could never please his mother, and that he might as well run away. He then recognized how his group work fit the same kind of early scene. The leader, in the classical TA way, said, "You never had permission to make it for yourself when you were a kid, and you have never given it to yourself. You have my permission." This procedure follows the permission and protection concepts of Pat Crossman (1966). She wrote that the therapist gives the patient *permission* to change and *protects* the patient from any harm while he is trying out his newly found strengths. The patient theoretically develops a new Parent in his head who is different from the old.

We at the Western Institute believe, however, that it is more important for the patient to do it for himself, and thus we handle the scene a little differently. We ask the patient, while he is in the middle of an early dialogue with a fantasied parent, what he feels when Mother says, "You never do anything right." We then ask him to respond to Mother. He may stay in his old position with his response, in which case we would ask him to be Mother, and to reply. Next, we would ask him to be himself and to reply. Eventually, he will most likely become disgusted with the scene, and say angrily, "I'm not going to listen to you anymore," or something similar, declaring his own autonomy. We then may ask him to respond one or more times, and during his response(s) we watch his body movements until we see that they and his words are congruent. This may all take place in the first 20 minutes of a group.

The most important work in the first few group sessions is to look for evidence of the patient's early decisions, and to allow him to reach an understanding of those early decisions. We are not at all interested in the "process" of a group; we do nothing to promote the intimacy that develops, except by indirection. We are not interested in the group as a "family"; i.e., we do not care who the patients pick out as Mother, Father, siblings, and Uncle John. We *are* interested in the bad feelings patients have, the games they play to develop those bad feelings, or to support them, the early decisions patients made about their lives, and how the games support those early decisions. We *are* interested in the life style, or script, and how the script is based on the early decisions and is supported by the games and rackets. We *are* interested in picking up evidence of the patient's original injunction from which the early decision was made, and the kind of strokes that the patient got to support the injunction.

Injunction-Decision-Games-Rackets Complex

I have given a full description of the injunction-decision-games-rackets complex in chapter 5, but a brief summary of the connections is relevant here.

Injunction

An irrational message that is called the *injunction* is given from a mother's or father's Child ego state. This injunction stems from the parent's own discomforts, hurts, and disappointments. For instance, a mother who does not want a child may not get an abortion, but wish she had; then, when the child is born, she may blame him for her own feelings, and tell him, nonverbally and verbally, that he is not loved, not wanted. She may say things like, "If it weren't for you, I would not have had to marry your father," which means: "Don't exist, and I will be happier." Thus she gives the child a "Don't exist" injunction. Another injunction may occur when a mother is disappointed that she got a little boy; therefore she dresses him in girl's clothes, with the injunction, "Don't be you," or, "Don't be a boy."

A mother may also want her son to act as a man, at five years old, and admonish.him to "take care of little sister," "don't cry," "don't play," or "there is too much work to do." The injunction is, "Don't be a child." (Most psychotherapists have this one.) A father may not like physical closeness, either with the child, his wife, or both, and the injunction is, "Don't be close."

A mother who may have wanted the pregnancy to end in abortion becomes guilty, and then overprotective by not allowing the child to swim, run, roller-skate, or climb trees. She says to father, "Go see what Susan is doing and tell her not to." The injunction is "Don't." A father may not want his daughter to be sexually provocative, because of his own fear of an erection when he sees his pre-teen girl; therefore he tells her not to wear sexy clothes, lipstick, and so forth. The injunction is, "Don't grow [up]." A father may be jealous of his son's ability to beat him at chess, or ping-pong, or wrestling, therefore he stops the activity and in effect says, "I won't play if you beat me." The injunction is "Don't make it."

Parents may not allow the child to tell how good he is, or to tell how really important he feels. The injunction is, "Don't be important." Parents who only show concern for the child by holding him and petting him when he is ill, communicate the injunction, "Don't be well." (This injunction describes the common phenomenon of a group member who stays forever.) There are other injunctions, but those just described are most important. Most destructive of course, is the "Don't be" injunction from which the child starts to develop depression and suicidal feelings.

Decision

When a child frequently hears and feels the injunction, "Don't be," and when he is getting negative recognition (strokes), he may decide that life is pretty tough, and say (in his head or aloud), "If things get too tough, I can always kill myself," or "I'll get you to kill me." These kinds of *decisions* may lead to a life style involving potential suicide, death by violence, death by coronary occlusion (while "showing" them), or death by accident. If a child doesn't make a decision to follow the injunction, he is not "stuck." (Our position differs here from the classical Berneian position in which most of us are victims if we get the injunction.) The child decides to go along with an injunction in order to survive, physiologically and psychologically, at that time and in that place. Some children get enough support from the opposite parent (e.g., "Don't listen to her. She is nuts. It has to do with her, not you.") not to have to obey the irrational order. Sometimes the child may get his support from a grandparent or even an older sibling, and then not yield to the injunction: not make a decision to follow it.

It is obvious that if a child did make a decision to kill himself, or not to trust, or not to be close, or not to grow up, or not to be a child, then he can remake it or change it at a later date, and begin to get out of his "bag." We look for decisions early in the group: "What did you decide to do to screw up your life, and what are you going to decide now to unscrew it?" We listen for all the evidence we can get to demonstrate the early decision. Some of it can be heard in the nonautonomous words people use; some of it can be picked up by listening to the change of pronouns in a sentence, such as "I am really tired. You work like hell and you never have any fun." With the first pronoun, *I*, we hear a report of how he feels; with the second and third, *you*, we hear the injunction being repeated: "You work like hell; you don't have fun." (Don't be a child.) We might ask the patient at this point, "Who told you not to have fun, and how did they tell you?"

Racket

The *racket* is a person's chronic bad feeling that supports the decision and the script. If a child decides at age four that someday, if things get too bad, he'll kill himself, and if the familiar feeling around his house is depression (that is, if he gets his strokes for being depressed, or sad), then the familiar feeling he has as he grows up is sadness. Thus, when he is grown he says, "I wouldn't know know to feel if I didn't feel sad." Other circumstances might start off a racket of anger, or frustration, or confusion.

For examples of rackets, listen to colleagues in staff meetings. One says, "That patient makes me so *angry*." Another returns, "You haven't seen anything. Y makes me so *anxious* when she calls at 3 A.M. threatening suicide." Another, a famous chest surgeon, says, "My terminal patients make me so *frustrated* when I can't cure them"; yet he accepts only difficult patients.

The individual, then, picks a feeling that fits with his original decision—perhaps that the atmosphere of the family and the kind of strokes he received are the way life will always be for him—and then looks for ways of supporting his feelings. The chest surgeon, for instance, not only was frustrated by his dying patients, but he also chose to be psychotherapist and clergyman to the families of those patients. Then he complained about their *frustrating* him when he could not solace them. "For 15 years," he said, "I have been asking how to deal with families, and no one has ever told me anything worthwhile." (Of course; he was in the frustration racket. When he decided to drop his frustrations, he began to feel good about his tremendous skill, rather than frustrated by the dying patient. He also left the counseling of the families to others who would allow them to mourn.)

People can maintain their rackets, then, by choosing situations, or actions, or behaviors that will support the rackets. At any given moment, a person can produce a fantasy he can use to "stay in the bad feelings." For example, while lying in bed after a happy, exciting, and satisfactory sexual encounter, a man can think of income tax due April 15, and be depressed; or he can think of the opportunities he missed last week in his business contacts, and feel saddened; or he can think of the hostility among nations and be depressed, thus taking himself out of the now-time and here-place into another time or another place in order to maintain his depressed feelings.

Early in a group, then, it is necessary for the therapist to create an environment in which the patient is rapidly aware of how he maintains old, chronic, bad feelings by his behavior, fantasy, or conscious selection. The therapist must then be prepared to confront him with alternate choices.

Game

The *game* was first defined by Berne as a series of transactions with a con, a gimmick, and a payoff. Here is an example of the start of a game. I was recently at an airport waiting for a plane. A child, probably 9 or 10 months old, was in a stroller parked across the aisle from me. His mother was reading the paper and ignoring him; he had a bottle in his hand. He looked at his mother, looked at the bottle, and dropped it on the floor. He then pulled at mother's pant-suit until she looked at him; she got up, and with a scowl, walked to where the bottle was, picked it up, shoved it at him, and sat down to read her paper.

He looked at the bottle, looked at her, pitched the bottle again, and once again pulled on her pant-suit. She looked up, swore, got up, picked up the bottle, thrust it at him, and said to him, "Hold onto the goddamn thing!" Then she sat down again and turned to her paper. He looked at her, looked at the bottle, threw it again, waited a few seconds, and once more pulled at her pant-suit. She looked at him, hollered at him, got up, got the bottle, shoved it in his mouth, and scolded him harshly. He cried and looked pained. She went back to her paper.

I interpreted the child's behavior as, "How do I get attention around here? Oh yeah, if I bug Mom, she will scold me, which is better than being ignored in this big strange place!" At this point, the child made a decision about getting strokes, even if the result was painful. This was just a little decision, but it may be the prologue to a major decision later on; that is, if mother scolds and ignores long enough, so that it seems to him that she is saying, "Drop dead," or "Don't be," or "Get out of here," at some point he will make another, more permanent decision: "If things get too bad around here, I can always knock myself off." He then can connect negative strokes, obtained by playing "Kick Me," with a small decision to play the game, with a larger decision to die someday if things get too tough. And, if he continues to play the game, things indeed will get too tough, and he will collect more and more reasons to kill himself. He may also find stories or fairy tales to support his position (from his decision), and may even begin to live out his real life according to that fairy tale. However, we don't use fairy tales to verify a script, but rather use them only to give us support for our hunches, based upon the information we receive. Neither do we use the fairy tale to set up treatment, which we consider to be an analysis of a displacement. For instance, if a man of 45 is depressed, we assume that he has made a decision at some point to kill himself, and we look for the evidence. We employ specific kinds of questions, leading to early memories, such as the following:

1. What is the myth of your birth? (I was unwanted, and besides I tore up my mother and caused her hemorrhoids.)

2. When you were born, what did they say about you when they looked at you.? (He's his father exactly.)

3. If you keep on with the present behavior and feelings, where will I find you in 5 years? 10 years? 20 years? ("A hermit." "You won't, I'll be dead.")

Joen Fagan (1971) asks the patient for his first memory. This is probably a good idea, but we are more inclined to ask: "And when did you feel depressed last year?" "When did you feel depressed in college?" "When did you feel depressed in high school?" "When did you feel depressed in grade school?" "When did you feel depressed before you attended school?" "When did you feel depressed the first time?" In other words, we do not ask: "Were you depressed?" But we ask: "When were you depressed?" Our belief is that when we begin with the most recent events and then go to the earliest events, we are far more apt to get associations and connections than when we start with the earliest events and work forward.

Once we have established or have a relatively strong indication (hunch) that there was a self-defeating decision, we may ask for a two-chair dialogue, and proceed with our hunches. Our method includes: obtaining the "early memory" by asking the patient to sit in the other chair and assume the position of his mother or father. In the role(s), he is to tell the patient (himself) what they feel or think about him—in the present tense. We then get the patient to respond and, often in a few transactions, pick up the early decision; e.g., "I'll get you even if it kills me." This patient may imagine himself driving his sports car at 90 m.p.h. down the mountainside while he is drunk and without seat belts, or playing third-degree "Rapo" and "Cops and Robbers"—from either the cop or the robber side.

We think that the early decision was made in response to both the stress and the way to get strokes in order to survive in that place at that time. We believe that the course of the script is more likely the result of following the pattern of games and strokes, and not so much the result of a preselected story or identification with a hero or heroine. Adopting a racket (the most common bad feeling) in service of the decision is the result of the experiences, the modeling, and the reinforcing strokes. If a child is sad, sees that mother is sad, gets strokes (negative or positive) for being sad, then his sadness fits into playing "Kick Me." And so disheartened by being depressed after the fourth divorce and the fifth firing, he finally can say, "After all that has happened to me, and all the bad feelings I have had, I am now entitled to kill myself."

In order to confront a patient's game playing, we first allow the game to move to completion, or, in the case of a lethal or third-degree game, we may ask the patient to imagine the end. We then *must* have a report from the patient of his bad feelings. (Without evidence of bad feeling, the patient may deny the game, and go underground with it.)

Earlier in this chapter I mentioned the game: "Why Don't You—Yes But." This is the most common game played in new groups. It has been thoroughly discussed by Berne in *Games People Play* and *Transactional Analysis in Psychotherapy*. In it, the player ends up feeling disappointed that no one (parent) ever does anything to help, and the other player, who usually plays from a rescue position ("I'm only trying to help"), also ends up frustrated that nothing he ever offers is really accepted. I saw this version played out while fishing on the river in Kashmir, India. I shall describe the conditions surrounding the game and the game itself.

I had to rent a flyrod and reel that included just enough back-up line and no fly-casting line, and all wet flies. Even with these odds and with three eager Kashmir fishermen surrounding me with nets, umbrellas, and advice, I caught a 17-inch rainbow trout on my first cast. This catch was difficult because I had to avoid my audience on my back cast, and cast a line that was made for following bait, not for carrying a fly. Despite the obstacles, I hooked the fish. Upon my bringing it close to the shore, one of my helpers rushed to the rescue with a landing net, and dislodged the fly. I quickly had to gill the fish with my finger to avoid losing him. "I was only trying to help, sahib," said my helper, looking crestfallen. I smiled (I had my fish) and said nothing. A few minutes later I landed my second, slightly smaller rainbow. And within another 10 minutes I landed a 10-inch, fat, brown trout. At this point, as my helper took the fly out, he said, "Why don't you use a peacock fly?" (Hell, I had just caught three fish on the Kashmir version of a wooly worm with white wings, but it was now a little worn, so instead of saying, "Yes, but I caught three," I decided to try the peacock.) I started to tie it on—I only trust my own knots—but my helper took it away from me and tied it. "That knot won't hold a big fish," I said. "But sahib, that's a good knot, why don't you use it?" I shrugged, made a few casts, and had a huge strike. I played the fish for a few minutes, and then he made a rush up the river, and swam away with my fly in his mouth as the knot pulled loose. I glared at my helper, who said again, "I was only trying to help." Once again he looked crestfallen.

In the first instance, I had not played. In the second instance, I had not initiated the game, but I allowed him to play when I didn't retie the knot, and my mild anger at the end, the remnant of my racket, proved that I had played; his crestfallenness proved that he had played.

But the game went on. He then tied a weight to my line (no self-respecting American fly fisherman would use a weight, because the American rainbows would see it. So do Kashmiri rainbows.) After 30 minutes of fruitless fishing, I waded across the stream, eluded my helpers, removed the weight and the second fly they had tied, tied on a wooly worm, and caught more trout, all of which I returned to the water before rejoining my friends for a rice and vegetable lunch. They were sure I had caught no more, and all of us were happy.

The incident illustrates some of the options of a therapist:

1. Play the game, but don't accept the payoff. (I caught the first fish and did not get angry with the helper.)

2. Play the game and accept the payoff. (I lost the fish and became angry.)

3. Ignore the game. (Cross the river.)

In (2), the therapist can confront the player and ask him if he has options other than the payoff; e.g., "Wow, I played; I understand it; I don't have to feel crestfallen, but I feel good that I understand."

Of course in a noncontractual situation I would be out of line to confront my Kashmiri friends; therefore, I did not confront them. That would have been playing "Hostalysis" (analysis with hostility as the motive), a favorite couples game when they first start in a TA group.

I have now discussed briefly some of the essential theory of TA: *decisions, injunctions, rackets, games, scripts.* I have briefly discussed therapeutic considerations: the nonselected group, ongoing vs. marathon groups, getting the contract, identifying rackets and games, looking for the primary decision, and creating an environment in which the patient can make a redecision. I have also briefly discussed some of the work done to teach the patient how to be aware of his incongruities and lack of autonomy, and how to become more congruent, and autonomous.

Redecisions

The essential difference between the kind of work done at the Western Institute and other therapy training centers is in the area of *redecisions*. The difference stems from the different philosophical position that we take compared with Berne's position and, I think in all fairness, compared with the position that most therapists take. I know few therapists who really believe that most patients can get well. We at the Western Institute do so believe, and we have a lot of evidence to support our belief. The Berne position is that people are primarily victims of their injunctions, that they are "scripted" by their parents, and to quote Eric in the book, *What Do You Say After You Say Hello?* (1972):

> The script matrix is a diagram designed to illustrate and analyze the directives handed down from the parents and grandparents to the current generation. These will, in the long term, *determine* the person's life plan and his final payoff. (p. 294) (Italics added.)

This sentence leaves no room for responsibility in the child to accept or reject the script. Eric described the injunction as follows:

For an injunction to be locked in solidly in the mind of a child, it must be repeated frequently and transgressions must be punished, although there are exceptional cases, as with battered children, where a single shattering experience can engrave an injunction for life.

The injunction is the most important part of the script apparatus, and varies in intensity. (p. 113)

Eric described injunctions as being inserted into the Parent of the Child, "where they act like a 'negative' electrode. This keeps Jeder from doing certain things such as talking or thinking clearly . . ." (ibid., p. 115). Over and over again, Berne saw the child with no choices, having electrodes "inserted," injunctions "inserted," etc.

Our position is that every child always has a choice. He bases his decisions on the information available and the way he interprets this information. He makes a decision in order to survive psychologically, and perhaps physically, in an environment that is not of his choosing and from which he cannot leave at an early age. He need not base the decision on the injunction, but perhaps most do because we can see no other way of getting along at that time.

If you take the position that the child does make a decision, then it is the Child in the patient who obviously can make a new decision. Thus, the focus of our work from the very beginning is to establish an environment in which the patient can in some way make a *redecision* for himself. Preferably, and for a real cure, this must come from his Child ego state, but we are willing to go along with one made from the Adult ego state, at first.

For example, let us examine a patient who has been suicidal for years. He is a psychiatrist who has made several suicide attempts, and was seen by us in a workshop in 1971. The first day of the one-month workshop we asked him if he were willing to state that he would not kill himself while in the workshop. He looked me straight in the eye and said, "I promise you I will not kill myself this month." I said, "I am not interested in promises; this is not for me, it's for you." He said, "I understand. I will not kill myself this month." For this period I was satisfied with this Adult decision and asked him if he were willing to do more work around that decision during the month. He stated that he was willing.

During some of the small-group work, which the trainees conduct with each other under our supervision, he did some more work in this area with one of our participating therapists, but he was still in his Adult. At the end of the work I asked both him and the therapist if they agreed to have him do some more work with me. They agreed. I asked him to fantasy that his mother was sitting in the chair across from him, and say to her, "I will not kill myself." He went through this exercise with his mother and father, with some rejoinders from them, and then looked at me and said, "I have done this before and I still don't feel any differently. I still am afraid that if things got too bad, I would try to kill myself again, and next time I won't just try." I responded, "Will you be that part of you that has not allowed you to kill yourself in the past—the part of you that didn't take quite enough pills, that allowed yourself to be found, that survived after your heart had stopped beating?" His eyes widened and he nodded. "Will you put the rest of you in the other chair and talk to the rest of you?" He said, "I will not let you kill me. I want to be alive and stay alive." He then screamed, "I will not let you kill me!"

"Will you be the other part of you?" I asked. He sat in the other chair and responded, "I hear you; you really want to live, don't you?" Then, crying, he said from the second chair, "I won't kill you. I won't kill myself." He then sat down in the first chair and said spontaneously, "I am the most powerful part of me and I will not let anything happen to me that ends in my death."

That was two years ago and my friend is still alive, is no longer depressed, and is doing well. He had made a decision as a child that if things got too tough he could always kill himself, and then he had made things get too tough. The experience of making a *redecision*, not just from his Adult, but also while in his Child ego state, was a most powerful one for him. How different this is from Eric's statement in *What Do You Say After You Say Hello?* (p.116) regarding the electrode as the therapist's decisive challenge. Neutralizing it requires enormous therapeutic power? The power is in the patient. Not in the therapist. It always was.

Countertransference and Transference

One last issue: our handling of transference and countertransference.

Countertransference

I insist that all our trainees are not only taught and supervised by us, but also treated by us. I know of no other way for the supervisor or training analyst to know really what is going on with his trainee or analyst unless he sees him as a whole person—not as a patient on one couch, while someone else sees him as an analyst at the head of another couch. I want to watch and to listen to my trainees as they switch from leader to patient, so I can hear how their countertransference gets in their way. For instance, I observe how a trainee in a group demonstrates frustration as he plays "Why Don't You—Yes But," and then gets caught in a beartrap (cf. Simkin, in Sager and Kaplan, 1972) with one of his patients in his own group and ends up frustrated. Or, how he plays "Kick Me" in the group (Child position) and then plays "Now I've Got You, You Son of a Bitch" (NIGYSOB) as leader (Parent position)—the two being parts of the same game. (Of course, his real parent, now incorporated into his Parent, kicked him as a child.)

I teach the trainee to use his own feeling responses to alert himself to what group members are doing. For instance, if he becomes aware that his foot is kicking, he may ask himself: "Does this have to do with me, or with the patient, or both? If it has to do with me, perhaps that patient's facial expression reminds me of my father, and I am in my own racket. If it has to do with him, what is he doing that I am responding to, and how can I use my feelings therapeutically?"

The following example is cited to illustrate the point: A counselor from the California Youth Authority walked into the first session of a weekend marathon with a beer in his hand. Three hundred and forty-seven of his co-workers from the C.Y.A. had been in our marathons, and all of them know that we allow *no* drinking during the weekend. I assumed, therefore, that he was attempting to set me up—with or without Adult awareness. I went through a series of questions in my head:

1. Is he playing "Kick Me"? (Answer: Probably.)
2. If he is, what will be his payoff? (Answer: My guess is, "He looks like an angry man.")
3. What decision does his anger fit? (Answer: My guess is, "I'll get you even if it kills me.")

4. What was his injunction? (Answer: Probably, "Don't be.")

There is obvious conjecture here, but I am using my feelings of very mild anger to start off a series of thoughts, and immediately drop my anger as I do so.

5. What shall I do? Alternatives:
    a) Kick him? (Answer: Too early.)
    b) Confront him with the game? (Answer: Too early.)
    c) Ignore him? (Answer: Beer *is* against the rules; won't do that.)
    d) Play it straight. (Answer: A–A)

Having decided (d), I said quietly but very straight to him, "One of the rules here is 'no drinking.'" He responded angrily: "Moralistic bastard!" (I now have answers to 1. (Yes); to 2. (anger); to 3. (I think I'm right; he'll try to get even.); to 4. (Yes, his injunction is "Don't be").

During the next 30 hours he played "Kick Me" most of the time, but refused to enter into any contract, tempted me in all kinds of ways to reject him ("Don't be"), to throw him out ("Don't be"), to fight with him ("I'll get even with you if it kills me"). I refused all ploys until 4 P.M. Saturday, when I was doing some very delicate and sensitive dream work. I had already asked two psychoanalysts in the group not to get into the dream work. When he came in with a very disruptive interaction, I said to him sharply, after five seconds of thought, "Shut up!" He did. When I was through the work, I turned to him and asked, "What did you feel when I told you to shut up?" Our exchange follows:

Patient: "You're a mother fucking son of a bitch!"

Goulding: "That's what you thought; what did you feel?"

Patient: "I'll get you, you bastard."

Goulding: "Is that a familiar feeling?"

Patient: "Damn right!"

Goulding: "What's the feeling?"

Patient: "Anger, you stupid prick!"

Goulding: "Are you often angry?"

Patient: "Always!"

Goulding: "Are you interested in knowing how you get there?"

Patient: "Nah!"

Goulding: "OK, when, or if you are, will you let me know?"

Patient: "Fuck you!"

Goulding: "It seems to me that you continue to ask me to be angry at you so that at some point I will be angry enough to ask you to leave. Does that fit?"

Patient: "Hey, yeah, it does. I've been fired or transferred from more jobs than anyone in Y.A."

Goulding: "Want to know how you do it?"

Patient: "I guess so."

Goulding: "Do you say that to get me off your back, or are you interested?"

Patient (*smiling*): "Go ahead, Doc, maybe I really will learn something!"

To summarize this brief interaction, I concluded that the trainee did have a "Don't be" injunction. He did decide, "I'll get even with you even if it kills me." He had been in many street and barroom fights, he drove a car recklessly and at high speeds, and so forth. He did some fine work, made a redecision to "live and enjoy" and, a year later, he had sold his sports car, achieved a professional advancement, and had not had a fight. Any feeling, then, of therapist toward patient that *could* be labelled countertransference can be used by a properly trained and skillful therapist.

Transference

The same patient, described under countertransference, can be used as an example to illustrate the handling of the transference phenomenon. Obviously, carrying the beer was a hostile act toward us, challenging our authority, which later on was shown as a familiar first move in a game. I allowed him to use me as a target until the proper time. I then asked him to use the same words that he had used towards me (saying them over again) to all members of his family, as we placed them (in fantasy) in various chairs. In this way, his negative transference was *immediately* worked through. The same procedure, with variations, is used in all cases of negative transference. We do not do a long-term analysis of the neurotic transference, but immediately put it where it belongs. In the same way, in training-group transactions with negative feelings, we very rapidly expose and confront the racket and the game, and then use the retrogressive method discussed above.

Therapist Qualifications

The Western Institute for Group and Family Therapy generally trains only people with advanced degrees in medicine, psychology, or social work. Ministers, priests, rabbis, and other members of the clergy who have advanced degrees, as well as people who do not have advanced degrees but who are being paid to do therapy in probation and parole work or other areas of corrections, are also trained.

Results

We have followed up our own and our trainees' patients and TA participants who have made no-suicide decisions over a five year period. So far, over 800 of these depressed people are reported to be alive, and we have not heard of a failure when our criteria have been strictly applied. In addition to these data, we have hundreds of letters in our files that attest to the effectiveness of TA.

Summary

Our primary interest is to create an environment in which the patient can discover that he supports bad feelings by games, fantasies, and displacement; that he holds onto his bad feelings to support his script and decisions in order to obey the injunctions that at one time he obeyed in order to survive psychologically and/or physically; that *now he obeys because it is familiar*; he thinks he doesn't know any other way, and that, for him, that's the way life is. He does, however, know other ways of behaving, and he can find other ways. He may be asked to try out other ways in the group, as a gestalt experience.

We object to long months or years of individual and/or group therapy that fosters dependence, maintains transference, and strokes sickness. We encourage rapid, decisive therapy, aimed at *immediate* autonomy, independence, and a feeling of accomplishment. We build upon strength, stroke strength, and let people know that even in their resistance they are strong and tough. But, we ask: "Is there not a better way to be tough?" We encourage persons to be loving, to be free of archaic demands and archaic injunctions, to live in the here and now, rather than the there and then, even while planning for a better tomorrow—not *trying* to progress, but *being* creative, spontaneous, autonomous, intuitive, intimate, aware, and enthusiastic, starting right now!

14   Redecisions in Marital Therapy

—R.L.G., and Ruth McClendon,[1]

For us, the successful treatment of a couple in a dysfunctional marriage requires working both with the interpersonal relationship, or the exterior system, and the intrapsychic selves, or the interior systems. By using a combination of transactional analysis and gestalt techniques, we create a permissive and protective environment (exterior system) in which change can occur quickly. In this therapeutic environment, each partner is encouraged to make redecisions for himself and herself; and then to make choices about their relationship in the here and now. Our approach is short-term and intensive rather than long-term and extensive.

The first step is to identify for ourselves the workings of the marital system, and then to help the two partners identify and change the system. This is a process of making explicit (bringing into Adult awareness) the interlocking acting, thinking, and feeling of the partners. Here we begin to teach the partners the value of the individual autonomy that each has given up, as evidenced by their language, both verbal and nonverbal. We confront them

First presented, in slightly different form, at a meeting of the American Psychiatric Association, Los Angeles, 1975.

[1]Ruth McClendon, a specialist in family therapy in private practice in Aptos, Calif., is president of the International Transactional Analysis Association.

at once with words like "can't," which more accurately would be "won't," and "the fight happened," which more accurately would be "I started the fight."

We clarify the process of how the partners react to or against each other in self-defeating ways. In this step we analyze ego states, transactions, and games. We look for the chronic bad feeling each partner has when participating in this back-and-forth system, a bad feeling we call a "racket." By focusing on this bad feeling, we are quickly able to help partners move toward autonomy rather than interlock unrewardingly with one another. In other words, we intervene in the game relationship, which is the support system for each other's pathology, and help them see the uselessness of that support.

Our main therapeutic principle is that each person is responsible for his or her own actions and *feelings*, although he or she may be choosing to respond in an automatic, stereotyped way. Our interventions are designed to expose the blaming in remarks such as "he makes me feel," or "she makes me do it," so that the partners take responsibility for their own individual feelings and behavior. Teaching the partners that each is responsible for her or his own feelings, and not the other's, is probably our major tool.

For example, a wife said to her husband, "You make me so confused." We first asked her to say it in another way; she then told her husband, "I don't understand what you want."

I said, "Isn't that what you meant when you said to him that he made you confused?"

She said, "Oh, yeah. Hey. Chuck, I don't understand what you want. Ask me in another way!"

After the partners have accepted responsibility, at least in their Adult, for their own actions, feelings, and lives, or, in other words, after the separation of the interlocking scripts and pathologies, we work with each partner as an individual. For the time being, the interpersonal work in clarifying how the two are stuck is finished. The question now is to investigate the reasons they have been choosing to relate in this dysfunctional way. This intrapsychic work is done through script analysis, followed by the most important process, the redecision work.

Redecision work is based on the principle that every person, when a child, makes some enduring choices about his or her life. The choices are based on a combination of things: the personal resources of the child; the information available from those doing the parenting; the parental demands, rational or irrational (the injunctions), made on the child; the interpretations the child makes of the information and demands; and the support received for those interpretations. Each child makes decisions about his or her life in order to survive psychologically, and perhaps physically, in that early environment; but the decisions live on. For instance, the grown-up John has patterned his whole life on the decisions he made about himself, and his worthwhileness, when a very young child. He still engages in a whole repertoire of feelings, thoughts, and actions to support those early basic decisions.

He even chooses his marriage partner, Sue, to play the same games he played with his original family, to stay in his old familiar spot. Sue, of course, chooses John for her own, similar reasons; and that is where every dysfunctional marriage system begins. Eric Berne called this a marriage contract of script. The contract of script is a secret agreement between John's and Sue's Child ego states to get together to make life the same old predictable thing. Through this nonverbal agreement John has, in choosing Sue, and Sue has, in choosing John, found a way to continue their same old patterns, games, rackets, etc.

They have sought to continue them because these patterns worked to get Sue and John what they thought they
wanted and needed. If John was angry enough, and
stormed around enough, sometimes his parents gave in
to his wants. If Sue cried enough, and was unhappy
enough, sometimes she got what she wanted. Now if John
storms out of the house, or Sue runs crying to her bedroom, the other gives in. If not, Sue can say, once again,
"You never understand me, I'll never get what I want, I'll
never make it. I might as well kill myself."

Redecision work, then, is essentially a change in the
intrapsychic system. It is an understanding, and a recon-
struction, of how marriage partners operate inside of
themselves individually. Thus the process is first to help
the partners to disengage from their currently destructive
system, and then to provide a protective environment
where each can make an individual choice about his or
her own life.

Let's return to the illustration of Chuck and Ann. She
said to Chuck, "I don't understand what you want," to
which he responded with a straight message. Anne next
said to a fantasied parent, at my request, the same words:
"I never understand what you want." I asked her to say
it two or three more times (encouraging her to get in
touch with some affect, and get into her Child ego state).
As she repeated the words, she started to cry, and said,
"I never can please you; I never know what you want. I
try and try, and I'm so confused; and I know I'll never
please you. I'll never please anybody. I might as well die.
I wish I were dead." I asked her if she really meant that,
and she said, "No, not now. I don't want to die. I want
to live, and be happy, and enjoy life. I'm tired of being
confused, and unhappy. Chuck, I don't want to kill myself. I won't kill myself. We will make it OK." At this
point, while in her Child ego state, while feeling as if she

were really talking to her parents, she switched, and made a redecision about living and enjoying. This was the first breaking through of an old impasse, which had started when she was a little child.

We take the final step in our treatment of a dysfunctional marriage after each partner has made his or her own redecisions, and is ready to choose how he or she will relate to the other in a new way. It is now a free choice for each partner, made with awareness of current needs, wants, and capabilities, rather than as a response to still unfinished gestalts from the past. In this step we are back to the interpersonal relationship, the exterior system, but the two individuals are now making their marriage a knowing choice, not a reflection of past decisions and systems. They are setting up their marital system as an intentionally patterned weaving, not a blind interlocking, tension-filled, pulling and pushing. As each partner chooses how he or she will act and feel in relationship to the other, they change their marriage to a functional system.

Back to Chuck and Ann. Ann has now done the most essential part of her redecision work. She has decided to live, to enjoy life, and to straighten out her transactions with Chuck, so that she is no longer confused, and no longer has to stay sad in order for her to get recognition from Chuck and to advance her original, suicidal script. But Chuck is still angry, although now that Ann is able to ask for clear messages, and to respond rationally to, or ask for clarification of, a negative response, he has less ammunition to fire back. We ask him to set up a dialogue with his fantasied parents, and to tell them about his anger toward them. As he gets into this scene, telling them how angry he is for all the things they did, and how they would not listen to him (as Ann "would not listen"), he begins to recognize the connection between his present anger and his archaic anger, and then, finally realizes that he is still being angry to get them to change, but not in the present; he wants them to change in the past. He recognizes the incongruity of this, and he is able to complete the ancient gestalt with them. He recognizes that his script decision included saying, "I'll get you to listen to me even if it kills me"; this is what he has also been saying to Ann, while giving her such confusing messages that she was unable to respond, thereby setting up a game in which he could stay angry. Now he asks Ann in clear language she can understand, and to which she can respond with a definite "yes" or "no." He is able to tolerate a negative response because now he understands that she is not responsible for his anger, and that she is willing to respond with a "yes" if it doesn't interfere with her own autonomy.

At this point, as Chuck is no longer trying to kill himself with frustration at not getting Ann to listen to him, his blood pressure starts to come down. In addition, both of them recognize that their many uproars in the past kept them from getting close, and that as children, they got further and further away from their parents because they couldn't trust them. In effect they had made the decision, "I'm never going to be close to you again," and had based their life with each other on this decision. They were then willing to redecide that they would be close, and not let disagreements get in the way of their closeness. In other words, they might still fight, but to solve problems, not to avoid closeness and play out their interlocking scripts.

15   Gestalt Therapy and Transactional Analysis

— R.L.G.

There are as many definitions of gestalt therapy as there are gestalt therapists. I have great difficulty when reading Perls, Shepherd, Fagan, Simkin, Polster, Laura Perls, and others, in coming up with a firm definition. Here's what *I* mean by "gestalt." When teaching my trainees, I draw the typical black circle on poster paper, and ask them to describe it. The first one usually gets tricky, and says that he sees a bunch of squiggly lines put together. Finally, someone says he sees a black circle on a white piece of paper on a redwood stand behind which is a wall and a stovepipe, in a barn. For me, it is also necessary to say that the barn is on a ranch on Mt. Madonna near Watsonville, in Santa Cruz County, California, U.S.A., a country on planet Earth, the third planet from the sun, in the Milky Way (or whatever we call this galaxy), in the universe. That, I say, is the gestalt process, the widening awareness of me, and of you.

This chapter describes how my gestalt techniques fit into the TA framework, a combined approach that my

---

First appeared in somewhat different form in *Handbook of Gestalt Therapy*, C. Hatcher and P. Himelstein (Eds.). New York: Jason Aronson, Inc., 1976. Used by permission.

195

wife, Mary, and I have developed. Most gestalt therapists, including Fritz Perls, believed or believe that the
patient integrates his therapy experience himself as he
breaks through the impasses, and that he doesn't need
any information from the therapist to integrate. Many TA
therapists, including Berne in the early days, and some
who attended the original San Francisco Social Psychiatry
Seminars, believe that if the therapist gives the patient
enough information about himself, his ego states, transactions, games, and script, he will use the information to
integrate, and make new decisions from his data processor
(Adult ego state). These practitioners don't think that the
patient needs a gestalt experience to integrate and to
change, or that he needs to experience himself moving
through an impasse.

I was fortunate enough, in the early 1960s, to work
with both Berne and Perls. I worked under Berne's supervision almost every Saturday for two years, attended
many of his seminars, and learned TA thoroughly. Both
Mary and I have also had a large exposure to the leading
gestalt therapists in the area. We all know that Fritz said
to lose your head and come to your senses. Most people
exposed to Berne knew that he called working with feelings "greenhousing," and he worked mostly with cognitive material. Well, I brought Fritz and Eric together at
my house in Carmel, and I bring them together in my
therapy. I believe, and have a great deal of evidence, that
both the gestalt experiences and the cognitive are important, and that the individual will do better with both than
with either separately.

The Polsters, Irv and Miriam, spoke of contact as the
first step in gestalt therapy; my contact with my patient
is my awareness of him, my awareness of me, and what
is happening between us. As I watch him and listen to
him, I am listening and watching for a series of contacts,

of awarenesses, that are defined in TA. I listen for the unpleasant feelings he has, and how he gets or maintains these feelings; I listen for the kinds of games he plays, and find out the kinds of fantasies he has, for it is in the playing of his games and in his fantasy life that he maintains himself in unpleasant feelings. I want to know what he was like when he was a little kid, and how he still behaves as that little kid. I want to know what his parents were like, and how he behaves, thinks, feels, and obsesses as they did. I want to know what kinds of messages they gave him, and how he reacted to those messages: what he said out loud, what he said inside his head, what he did, in response, and what he is still doing, thinking, and feeling as he did then. I want to find out how he is blocking himself, maintaining himself in impasses, and avoiding intimacy, autonomy, creativity, spontaneity, and growth.

Now, I don't want to learn all those things in a sterile, history-taking, boring way. I want to learn about him a in a live, exciting process that is part of our engagement, part of our contract. I want him to learn these things about himself as I learn them; I want him to come up against his impasses, and deal with them; either to admit an impasse, or to break through it. It is his choice, not mine, whether to stay in it or go through it. It is important that he knows the relevance of his impasse to his unpleasant feelings or "rackets," his games, his fantasies, his life script, his early decisions that he made, in order to survive in his environment, in response to the overt and covert messages that he received from his parents and other important figures in his life. These messages we categorize in TA as injunctions and counterinjunctions. Impasses are first-degree (relating to the counterinjunctions), second-degree (relating to the injunctions), or third-degree (relating to the patient's own awareness of self, of what he feels himself to be, of what he experiences as being part of him, and not directly related to the outside messages and pressures). It is our position, and here we differ from many gestalt therapists, that a firm cognitive understanding of the relationship of the impasses to the distant past (the ways in which the patient has not completed old experiences and is still trying to do so through avoidance, blocking, or inappropriate behavior) will help him to change.

As we work, then, moving towards impasses as we explore his universe, we begin to teach him a method of being autonomous, by asking him to be aware of all the ways he gives away his autonomy. We usually don't listen to him talking *about*, but ask him to talk *to* whomever he is talking about. If he is talking about his wife, we ask him to talk to her. If she is not in the room, we ask him to pretend that she is. If he is talking about his mother, we ask him to bring her into the room, and talk to her as if the event were happening right now, in the room. We know that many gestalt therapists will only deal with the immediate present, asking the patient to work in the here and now without relating to the past. We don't agree with that position, and we ask the patient to be aware of his past as it relates to the here and now, to be aware of his decisions, the injunctions and counterinjunctions, and all the related bits.

So, we work only with I-Thou transactions, in the here and now, and not with talking about history. We bring the history into the present, and then the work becomes exciting. The patient, as he relives an old scene in which he is stuck, gets together the memory with the affect, and begins to relive the scene. He is overcome by his sadness or by his anger. He works with the scene until he either completes it, or becomes aware that he is not willing, at this time, to complete it. Completing means finishing it, not being in the impasse anymore, either in the present or in the original impasse.

For example, a woman of 40 who sounds and looks like she is only 10, may go back to a scene where she feels as lonely as she confesses to feeling in the present; she may go back to a scene in her childhood when she is 10 years old, when her father is dying. She won't say good-bye to him, because she doesn't want to admit that he is dying; and after he dies, she refuses to mourn, but pretends that he will come back if she is a good girl and waits for him. She thus freezes herself into a Sleeping Beauty script, in which she stays a little girl, sleeping in the tower waiting for Santa Claus, or the Prince (really father). Until she actually gets back in the scene, deals with her unfinished business, says good-bye and tells her fantasied father that she is not waiting for him anymore, she will stay a little girl. She must go through the scene, sometimes closing the casket, throwing dirt in the grave, saying good-bye. If she backs away from the completion, still holding on to the magic, she will not let herself grow up to claim her sexuality and her sensuality. She will stay waiting for someone to find the pure princess and take away her loneliness. The only person who will show up is a burglar.

If she completes the scene, finishes the good-byes, and the mourning, she will free herself to grow up and claim her maturity. In either case, we want her to be sure to understand the nature of the impasse, what the threads are that bind her to her past, and what she did to break through, if she did.

As we connect the affective experience with the cognitive understanding we use TA. We may draw on the blackboard or poster paper the threads, the connections. We think that it is OK to tell the patient something, unlike some gestalt therapists who say they are insulting the patient if they give him information.

A patient's internal dialogue may start with body gestures. A recent trainee, with us for a month, started to work on allowing himself more fun, more spontaneity, more freedom, to be in what some transactional analysts call the Natural or Free Child. As he started, he put his finger in front of his mouth. "Be your finger," I said; and he said, as his finger, "Shut up. You can't be free." The dialogue that developed was between his archaic Parent, who said, "Don't be childlike. I don't like your noise when you act like that. You make me nervous," and his Child, looking for a way to break through and be more free. He became more excited as he responded, and by the time the dialogue ended, he was bouncing in his chair; his voice was louder, firmer, more melodious, and his whole body position had changed markedly.

All gestaltists know of the work that I am talking about. Here I am putting the impasse work into a specific framework, in which the trainee-patient's movements through the stuck places are related to the injunctions, decisions, games, rackets, and script. Even if he doesn't get through this time, seeing the relationship helps him to work when not in the session, to come back the next day and work again, to recognize how his behavior, when he refuses to join a poker game in the evening, is his response to a "Don't have fun,' or "Don't be a child" injunction; and his decisions to grow up before he was ready to, and to take care of others (siblings then, psychiatric patients now), were designed to inhibit his freedom in the service of pleasing mother or father. Each time he throws off the inhibition, joins in and has fun, he is making a tacit redecision from his Child to ignore the old messages and enjoy himself more, and his new behavior reinforces the new position rather than the old position. The stroking or recognition he used to get from others, for doing his old thing, is now changed into stroking from the workshop members for doing the new, and his growth is speeded.

In a workshop years ago, with Fritz and Jim Simkin leading, I did an awareness-continuum exercise. When I was finished Jim asked me what I was experiencing. I said, "It was great," referring to the awareness experience. Jim raised his eyebrows, I caught on, and said joyously, "*I* am great." I repeated that two or three times, and kept repeating it all week, to the amusement and support of the rest of the group. That moment had marked a change in my life for me.

I also used my knowledge of TA to put the experience into perspective, to see how I had been depriving myself in many ways because I had been taught not to brag, not to claim myself, not to be important, not to be selfish, and other kinds of "don'ts" that I had used to prevent myself from enjoying me and my life to the fullest.

Here we are back to the importance of combining the emotional with the cognitive. I had had a peak experience, and I had put my knowledge of TA and of my own injunctions and early decisions to work for me in making some new decisions.

I especially did this the last day, when Fritz noticed I was filling my eyes with tears. He asked me if I were all right. I said that I was, that I was experiencing myself as water boiling in a pot, about ready to blow off my lid.

"Be the lid," he said, and I, as the lid, said: "Be careful, Bob. Quiet down."

Then, as Bob, I responded, "I don't need you, lid," as I both understood and felt what I had been doing to myself. I became the hot water, and then the steam, expanding into the air, into space—and for the first time in my memory was in touch with my uniqueness, my power, my ability.

The cognitive information that I already had about myself allowed me to make other impasse breakthroughs, so that I freed myself from former inhibitions. The "working through" that traditional group therapists talk about, and that they claim occurs as the patient works on and on in the group, I did as part of my living experience. I had to change some of my environment to maintain a better support system around me, because I would have had great difficulty in staying in such a fulfilling awareness of self had I remained in the old environment. And so I changed it.

The use of the passive voice, the subjunctive mood, and words like *it* instead of *I*, may lead to many awarenesses if the therapist hears them, understands their relevance in the injunction-decision complex, and leads the patient to a new discovery of his prospects for autonomy. Although purely gestalt work may get him through the immediate impasse, the further use of TA to relate the impasse to the archaic impasses enables the patient to make better use of the experience. Also, as the patient understands that the original decision to diminish his own importance, to play second fiddle, or take a seat in the back of the bus, was made because it was the only solution that he could find at that time, in that place, and with those people. It was thus an extremely useful tool for him. As he works through some of the earlier impasses, he begins to be in touch with the power that he had then, with the power that he used to survive, to stay alive, or sane. As he reclaims that power for himself, he can more easily give up the old position, now inappropriate, and experience a new power for growth, for broadened awarenesses. As long as he is downgrading himself for his "faults," he stays in a harassed, inferior position from which it is difficult to move. When he can say, "Wow, Dad, I beat you after all, and I don't need to do that anymore," he can move from the archaic to the new position far more easily.

Another helpful way of integrating gestalt and TA is in the confrontation of games. Here is a typical example from one of our training groups. A therapist from Europe was criticizing, inappropriately, my critique of other therapists who were working with fellow trainees as clients. Later she said, "I am often very critical of people, and I usually end up feeling bad, because someone usually criticizes me for being critical. I'm beginning to understand why I do that. I do it to keep feeling bad; it isn't right for me to feel too good, or something bad will happen. If I say something good to people, I will in some way harm them. When I was a little child, criticisms were all I got. No one noticed me when I was a good little girl." She had her hands out, with one hand higher than the other, moving them in the air, and with the higher, left hand making sharp, downward motions. I asked her to be her left hand. She said, "This is the part that criticizes, and my right hand is the part that sometimes strokes positively." She then started a dialogue between the two, ending up by stroking her left hand with her right hand; as the days passed, she became less and less critical.

Another trainee asked a colleague if he would take him to Carmel over the weekend. The second trainee, Jim, who didn't like Joe, said no. Joe then pouted, feeling hurt, sad, and abandoned. We asked him when the last time was that he felt abandoned, and had him relate the scene in the present tense. He first talked to the girl with whom he had living most recently, and who had split from him. Then he talked in fantasy to his ex-wife, who had also left him; then to a series of girl friends who had left him prior to his marriage. Each time we had him talk in the present tense. Then he put his mother in the chair in front of him, in fantasy, and talked to her about her abandoning him when he was nine, and later killing herself. During this scene, also in the present tense, he was finally able to relive the moment in which she had said goodbye to him. He told her of all his resentments, as well as of his appreciation of her, and finally he was able to close this old scene satisfactorily.

Since then he has stopped setting himself up to be abandoned, or refused, or rejected, and if turned down, he no longer sits around feeling depressed and rejected. He no longer tries to get rid of mother so that he can try to bring her back by letting her know how sad he is. Over and over he had set up situations in which the only reasonable choice for his wife, or girl friends, or any friend, would have been to leave, or to say no.

In each case the game was obvious. In the game with Jim, he already knew that Jim had asked one of the women to go with him, and had already turned down someone else, so that a part of him had the information that Jim would not be likely to take him. Thus, when his ostensibly straight message was "Take me along," his secret message was, "Turn me down," and the chances were very good that Jim would. When Jim said "No," in response to the secret message, Joe then took his payoff in sadness, feeling abandoned, and saying to himself, "No one loves me; they all turn me down," his repeated statement about himself and others. By using the feelings he produced at the point of payoff, to take himself back into the past, he completed the archaic gestalt.

Probably the greatest difference between other gestaltists and ourselves is our approach to feelings. Most gestaltists I know encourage people to get into the depth of their feelings, in order to move out of them. We see that people use their fantasies, and their games, to maintain themselves in negative feelings, and that it is not necessary to abreact with utmost zeal. People have been going around from encounter group to marathon to encounter group displaying their wildest rage or deepest sorrow for years, and not changing a bit. They hold on to their anger or anxiety from the past in a magical effort to change the past. Our primary therapeutic effort is to encourage patients to be aware of the feelings they are repressing before letting them go, and to let go of those inappropriate feelings they are expressing, once they recognize how they bring them on themselves.

Therapists attending my lectures sometimes question my statement that we make ourselves feel bad, that no one but me is responsible for my feelings. I then like to ask all in the room to close their eyes and remember the last time they felt angry, or anxious, or depressed because someone was "making them" feel bad. I ask them to get into the scene, to experience their feelings, and then to have another fantasy, in which they are somewhere they most want to be, doing what they most want to do. Almost no one, a minute later, is still in the unpleasant feelings he or she had given themselves. The lesson is obvious.

Doing a regressive scene is often helpful for patients in letting go. As they remember the scene, and get into a dialogue and begin to cry, or become angry, I might say, "Will you tell him/her that you are going to stay angry/sad until he/she changes?" This statement usually brings an end to the unpleasant feelings, and the patient says, "AH HA!" If he or she stays in the feelings, the next line is, "Are you willing to tell them that you will stay angry until they change the past?" Then there is almost always an "AH HA!" which here comes with the cognitive *and* affective recognition of how ridiculous it is to expect anything to change in the *past*, that the past can't change, and that all these years the anger has been at the parents for what they did years ago. A phobic in treatment with us recently had this AH HA experience when he recognized that he had dropped his phobia of heights because his testicles no longer "scrunched" when he was on the roller coaster at Santa Cruz. "AH HA!" he exclaimed. "Even my balls know I'm not scared anymore."

As people make themselves feel bad by going into the past, or the future, or somewhere else (for example, obsessing at night about how to pay the bills) they learn to change fantasies. A simple switch is to change from obsessive thinking to sexual fantasy. Another way of moving from unpleasant feelings is to evaluate, first, the feeling. What is it, and what is it in response to? Did I really do something, or did someone else really do something, or is it fantasy? If fantasy, change or drop it. If there was a real happening, is there anything I can do about it now? If there is nothing, then the feeling is of no use, and I can drop it. If there is something I *can* do, do I want to do it? If I do, then I'll do it, and drop the feeling. If not, the feeling is to no avail, so I'll drop it.

For instance, at the moment of writing this, I am angry at IBM, because my Mag Card 2 Typewriter just ate up the card these words were recorded on, and I am typing them over. When I am through with this page, I will call IBM, express my dissatisfaction, and then go back to work, and drop the anger.

One of the most important pieces of therapy that we learned from Eric Berne is the negotiating of the therapeutic contract, and the awareness of the psychological contract. The goal of the therapeutic contract, of course, is what the patient offers to do for himself, to change; the goal of the psychological contract may be the secret resolve by the Child not to change anything. The latter is usually stated in what I call the first "con," when I first hear the Child's statement that he has no intention of changing. For instance, the statement, "I want to work

on my anxiety," sounds great, but in fact if it is not chal-
lenged, that is exactly what the patient will do: work on,
and on, and on, and never change anything.

Simkin called this "bear trapping." It needs to be confronted with, "Are you just going to work, or are you
changing something?" The therapist's question, "Are you
willing to do an experiment, or an exercise?" is often met
with "I'll try," and that is exactly what he does: try. Do
you know the difference between "trying to shit" and
"shitting"? By my chair I keep a large cow bell, which I
ring vigorously when anyone says "try." It's the best behavior modification that I know; very few people in the
workshop say "try" more than once.

There are hundreds of clues to the first con: "Would
like to," "perhaps," "just," "maybe," "you know," "can't"
(which usually means "won't"). "Should" and similar
words usually mean that we are about to be offered a Parent contract. "I should quit drinking," means, "I don't
intend to, but my husband wants me to." We are wary
of Parent contracts, of course, and often ask "why?" when
we suspect one. Although "why" is usually a poor word
in gestalt therapy, sometimes it flushes out the con, in
the early work.

We are adamant about getting contracts in most cases,
although sometimes we settle for exploration for a while.
I teach my trainees, in the small group exercises we do,
to work no more than 20 minutes, so that they have to
sharpen up their ears. If they don't get through an impasse in 20 minutes, they aren't going to get through it
today, because they haven't been listening. The Polsters
have written about not confronting every con, and I understand their intent, but until a therapist knows which
ones to let by, he had better confront them all. The Polsters are master therapists; not many others are.

We don't accept, "I want to understand myself better," either. Fritz would have called that an elephant-shit contract, and there certainly would be a lot of it around if we let that one go through. People work for years "trying" to understand themselves better, and nothing ever happens. We want a contract that calls for specific changes: in behavior, in feelings, in thinking; changes that are testable. Although we want the patient to understand (understanding does help—that is a main point of this paper), understanding about self without any connection to symptom change is not a valid contract goal. At the same time, we do not always insist that the patient understand what was going on in the past; sometimes we cure a phobia, for instance, with desensitization, without the patient having any idea of why she is phobic.

About a year ago a woman had a cockroach phobia. I usually do some work with second- or third-degree impasses in my phobia work, and in this case I attempted to set up some dialogues, feeling certain that the phobia was displaced from a fear of sex. We got nowhere. I finally stopped, and asked her if she were willing to do some desensitization.

She was, so I asked her to relax in the chair, raise her left forefinger when she became scared, and her right forefinger when she was not scared. She agreed, and I proceeded to march a fantasied cockroach in through the door, closer and closer to her, until she raised her left finger. I marched that cockroach in and out, in and out; then two cockroaches, then four, then a platoon, then a company, then a battalion, then a regiment, until she finally laughed, got up, picked up an imaginary broom, and swept the army out. A year later she wrote me that she not only had dropped her phobia, but also had a much better sexual relationship with her husband! My guess was right, I think, but she was not willing to work on that at the time.

Sometimes the patient gets the information in a flash of recognition, an "AH HA" experience without any reference to his injunctions, decisions, games, or script, and makes a redecision, from his Child, in the process. For instance, a minister here for a workshop said he wanted to do something about his sexual behavior. He offered girls sex, and then somehow secretly said to them, "Don't take me up on it." He also masturbated but stopped himself before ejaculating. I asked him, "Always?" No, he finished sometimes. Well, obviously if he finished sometimes he could finish all the time, and he didn't have to know why in order to change. He stopped in order to harrass himself, and also because he was afraid.

I decided that I would go ahead and work with him, even though I could have asked him to experiment tonight with masturbating to a conclusion and reporting his experience tomorrow. I asked him to sit in a different chair, and be the adolescent, imagining that he was masturbating. In that chair he stopped before ejaculation. Then I asked him what he was feeling. He responded, "Good. I'm a good boy."

"What else are you feeling?" I asked.

"Irritated that I didn't finish." Now I asked him to sit in the other chair and imagine himself finishing. From that chair he reported feeling contented, but scared. I asked him to move back to the first chair, and to say "I'm scared that I will. . .," and to finish the sentence.

"I'm scared that I will die," he said. I asked him to sit in the second chair again, where he had allowed himself to come to orgasm. "How many times have you died?" I asked him.

"AH HA!" he exclaimed.

"Sit back in the first chair," I said. "Now, say, 'I'm scared I'll die again.' " "I will not," he said laughing. "I'm done."

When the minister dropped his fear, when he broke through the impasse, both cognitively and emotionally, he *suddenly* recognized that all those years he had been setting up "Rapo" games, and refusing to masturbate to orgasm because of an early fear of dying, if he "did that." The point is, he could have gone ahead, as he had done many times, masturbating without completing the above gestalt. He got in touch with his mother's crazy message that he would die if he masturbated, which he had so taken in that he had forgotten the message, and only remembered the scared feeling. This was a third-degree impasse, with a memory of a scary face, rather than of actual words. I suspect he introjected the message when a very small child.

Many gestalt therapists, including Perls and Erv Polster, use themselves a great deal in what I would call setting up deliberately a transference with the patient. Fritz would do all kinds of maneuvers to frustrate the patient; I remember one well-known gestaltist who hit him with a chair. We prefer, usually, not to invite a transference, although of course we do use ourselves. We are much more likely, however, to endeavor to keep out of the work, and to let the patient do his work against himself, by setting up dialogues, by keeping I-Thou transactions going, by saying "any more?" instead of "tell me." Thus we hope that the patient, instead of resisting us, will resist himself, recognize the impasse when he gets to it, and either break through or stay stuck at the point of impasse. We prefer that he battle against his own internal Parent, instead of with his transferred "parent," us. A clear knowledge from a TA standpoint of where the impasse is is most helpful to the therapist in establishing a useful dialogue.

One more point about TA and gestalt I think is important. In my experience, those TA therapists using only a cognitive approach, with Berne's sequence of analyzing ego states, then transactions, then games, and then scripts, thus ending in the patient's firm understanding of self, may result in a patient changing overt behavior but not feeling much better. Gestalt alone, on the other hand, may end with patients feeling great about themselves, but not changing behavior, and perhaps remaining perfect shits. Our use of both, so that the patient does a great deal of experiential work *and* understands his life script, is more likely to change both his behavior and his feeling. That at least has been our experience with the hundreds of therapists we have worked with over the past 13 years, as we moved more and more into a shotgun approach of TA, gestalt, behavior modification, and anything else we learn or develop that works. Group 8 in the Lieberman, Yalom and Miles (1973) study (*Encounter Groups: First Facts*) seems in some degree to support this position also.

To sum up, we use all the gestalt techniques we can muster to allow patients to work through their impasses, which they can relate to their archaic impasses. We believe, and we have a great deal of clinical evidence, that the more cognitive information the patient has about his connections from the present to the past, the more he uses the information to change. If he can connect his earlier scenes to his present feelings, and will make new decisions from his Child ego state while in the scene, he will then use these redecisions to change his life in the present. Each impasse resolution of both present "stuck places" and archaic "stuck places" brings more freedom, so that the patient can continue to grow, and to expand his boundaries and awarenesses.

16 Injunctions, Decisions, and Redecisions —R.L.G. and M.M.G.

After recognizing that in our work with patients we kept hearing the same relatively few injunctions, we decided to classify them. Our list today is almost the same as the one we devised in 1966: *"Don't be"; "Don't be you (the sex you are)"; "Don't be a child"; "Don't grow"; "Don't make it"; "Don't"; "Don't be important"; "Don't be close"; "Don't belong"; "Don't be well (or sane)"; "Don't think (don't think about X [forbidden subject;]"; "Don't think what you think (think what I think)"; "Don't feel (don't feel X [mad, sad, glad, etc.]"; "Don't feel what you feel, (feel what I feel)."*

At first we did not recognize the distinction between injunctions and Child decisions; during this period, like other TA therapists, we looked for "exact words" of the injunctions and an 'exact scene' in which the injunction was given. We saw that, although patients remembered remarkably similar early scenes and injunctions, each individual reacted uniquely. Our clients were not "scripted." No one is "scripted." Injunctions are not placed in people's heads like electrodes. Each child makes decisions in response to real or imagined injunctions, and thereby "scripts" her/himself.

First appeared in somewhat different form in *Transactional Analysis Journal*, 1976, 6(1), 41-48.

People of all ages make Adult (A2) decisions daily. These are time-limited, and usually are not locked into the individual's personality structure. A very young child who wants to get out of a playpen uses acquired Adult information and Adult thinking processes, plus trial and error, to unscrew a side and make the pen "fall down," or piles up the toys and climbs over the top. If something goes wrong such as getting punished for the activity, she or he may make an A1 decision in response to a "Don't ever do that again" internalized injunction. If the child fails, or gets hurt, a decision may be made by the Little Professor (A1) even without an injunction from outside. The Child, in this case, creates both the injunction and decision. If the child receives much positive support for the activity, she or he may make an A1 positive decision about continuing to be a genius at figuring things out, using one's hands, being creative, etc., in response to positive Child messages from parents.

Adult decisions are made cognitively; they fit for a specific situation, and are easily changed with new data. We believe that Child decisions are most often made when the person is unable to get good responses to, or good solutions from Adult decisions. This seems to be especially true when Adult decisions are triggered by Free Child desires. The Free Child wants out of a playpen to explore more fully, or to be with other people. When getting out becomes sufficiently dangerous, threatening a loss of love, physical pain, or gross disapproval, a negative Child decision will be needed to curb both the Free Child and the Adult ability to make reality-oriented decisions. The youngster may need to decide "I can't get my needs met," "I'll pretend I'm not here so they won't hurt me," a despairing "I'll get them to kill me," or some other decision. Of course, the infant hasn't these words, so the behavioral and feeling decisions at first are wordless.

Eric Berne described the stack of coins, which remain neatly stacked until one coin is skewed, and from then on the pile cannot be straight. In just such a way, early decisions, if unchanged, may skew later decisions. An Adult decision to learn how to hit a ball with a bat successfully involves a host of everyday decisions about finding others who are willing to play, finding the necessary equipment, watching, practicing, and learning. A Child decision may evolve: "Wow, I'm the best!" or, if unsuccessful, an Adult decision, "I'm going to work at this until I'm as good as the others," or a Child decision, "There's no use in my trying—I never do anything right." A child who has already decided not to be aggressive, competitive, or clever, because of lack of success as far back as playpen days, may use baseball to explain and fortify the old decision, or may make new, more tragic decisions, such as, "If things don't get better, I'll kill myself."

As therapists, we are interested in the Child decisions that still "skew the pile" for our patients, and our therapy is based on creating a therapeutic environment in which patients may redecide from the Child ego state. The alternative, Adult decisions and redecisions, are appropriate in contract setting and may serve temporarily as a watchdog over behavior, but are not truly corrective.

Injunctions and Decisions

1. "Don't be," or "Don't exist." This may be given directly or overtly, as with attempted murder, or abandonment. (The rich use expensive schools and summer camps instead of foster homes or orphanages.) "Don't exist" may be implied by brutality, and by indifference. Mostly, children hear that they weren't wanted or that the parents

would have had better, happier lives "if you hadn't been born." Examples: "I only stay with him (or her) for the sake of my children" means that Father or Mother could have a happy life if the child or children didn't exist. "If it weren't for your coming along when you did, your father could have finished medical school." "I could have been an opera star." "Your mother wouldn't be in a mental hospital." "She died giving birth to you." "He's our little accident." "I never wanted more than two children, but we're Catholic." "He came too soon," ". . . too early," ". . . too late," ". . . in the worst of the depression." "They had to get married because of that child." "He'll never replace the one who died . . . that one is our angel."

(Many parents may say these things for effect; that is, to get a child to change behavior, or to appreciate them, or because they are mindlessly reeling off the tapes of what was said to them by their parents. The injunctions, then, may be contradicted by "I love you and want you" messages from the parents, and the child makes his own decisions based on his own evaluation of the situation.)

Notice that some of these messages imply that the child brings himself into the family, and that the birth is the child's fault or responsibility. In the Child ego state, this responsibility is often accepted.

When I hear a "Don't be" injunction (or any other), I say, "Be there. What's the scene? What are you deciding?" Some children decide, "You're wrong, I am valuable." Others make up a fantasied parent somewhere who really loves them; and some say "You didn't want me, but Daddy [or Grandma, or my teacher] does." Some work extra hard, staying with the counterinjunctions, while saying "Even if you don't love me, I'll show you I'm valuable." Some become little psychiatrists or priests, as they study the family and attempt to cure it, while saving their own lives by recognizing that the pathology is not of their doing.

However, if the injunction is accepted, the child may make any one of a number of decisions: (a) "If you don't change, I'll kill myself." (That is how blackmailers are born, who threaten suicide when spouses leave, therapists vacation, etc.) (b) "If things get too bad I'll kill myself." These people make things too bad and count only the negative stamps.) (c) "I'll show you even if it kills me" (d) "I'll get you even if it kills me [with guns, or cars]." (e) "I'll get you to kill me." (f) "I'll almost die (over and over again) to get you to love me."

Sometimes, in order to escape lethal decisions, the child makes decisions that are responses to other injunctions, such as, "I'll never again be close to anyone, so I won't have to kill myself."

Killing oneself, of course, can be deliberate or "accidental," such as not getting medical care in time, using a car as a weapon, volunteering for combat duty, etc.

2. "Don't be you (the sex you are)." If the parent who gives such a message genuinely values heterosexuality, the child may decide to accept other, better messages. The child may decide not to listen, and not to feel bad. One male therapist mentioned recently that his mother wanted him to be a girl, and that she played a great deal with him, with dolls, and by "cooking together." He remembers the exact day he looked out the window and recognized that other boys play outside, and do not play with their mothers in the kitchen. He marched out, announcing, "I am a boy from now on," and did not return to the dolls or the kitchen. The child may go ahead doing the sex-appropriate activities but never feel good about self. For example, the girl may play with dolls, marry, and keep house, but continue to feel second-class, knowing that she is a "disappointment." There are many other

possible decisions, including keeping or acquiring a first name that hides the true sex, cross-dressing publicly (if girls) or privately (if boys), choosing "the other sex's occupation," or choosing transexual surgery. Some simply continue lifetime private wars against the other sex.

Many appreciate having received this injunction. In the days when girls were supposed to stop thinking and achieving as soon as they married, some girls used the steam from "Don't be a girl" to have rich, successful, professional lives. And some men used the "Don't be a man" to permit themselves a gentleness and artistic appreciation they might not otherwise have had.

3. "Don't be a child." This is given most often to the oldest, who is supposed to be responsible for the younger children, may not fight back, and is admonished, "You are too old to do [whatever childlike behavior the parents don't like]." The child may grow up to be a therapist who doesn't remember how to have fun. The decisions may be, "I'll never do that [the behavior] again," "I'll take care of you [happily or resentfully]," "I'm the only one who can manage," etc. Examples: A man remembers when his dying father said, "Take care of the rest." From age 12 to the present he has been taking care of his brothers, his mother, and everyone else who "needs" something from him.

Sometimes this injunction is: "Don't have needs," and a decision then may be to deny self, or to go crazy in order to get needs met.

4. "Don't grow." There are several injunctions that we include in the "Don't grow" category: "Don't grow beyond infancy" (see the Schiff [1969] articles on schizophrenia), "Don't grow beyond [a certain age,]" "Don't think," "Don't be sexual," "Don't leave me."

Youngest children are most often told not to grow: "You are too young to do that." They are told this by parents repeatedly and by older siblings, and they see the repeated demonstration of their inabilities when compared with the older people in the house. Some accept, and remain in the "cared for" rather than the "caretaking" role, and some fight back, saying "I'll prove I should have been born first."

Priests may accept both "Don't be sexual" and "Don't be a child" messages. Sometimes "Don't be a child" and "Don't ever leave me" messages are accepted, and the child grows fast but remains with the parents to take care of them. Other times, "Don't grow" and "Don't leave me" go together, and the child remains at home to be cared for.

Girls may be told not to grow sexually, because father is afraid of his own repressed sexual urges, or because father hates women and loves girls.

Sometimes it seems that the injunction is self-inspired in reaction to a trauma that did not include a "Don't grow" message, as when a girl becomes a Sleeping Beauty while waiting for an absent father to return.

5. "Don't make it." This injunction is given by the jealous Child of a parent and it means, "If you are more successful, talented, beautiful or intelligent than I, I will not love you." Particularly we see this injunction given by fathers to sons in work relationships. Father, exasperated, says, "You never do anything right," rather than, "Do it right." The son decides, "I'll show him" and works extra hard as he successfully fights back against the injunction; or says, "I'm just naturally no good at [father's specialty]," or "He's right—I can't do anything right," and becomes in his own eyes, and perhaps in others', a failure. I suspect a decision not to make it when anyone has an "ABD" degree (all but dissertation), instead of a PhD. Some people "honor" their parents by feeling unsuccessful. They

keep upping their goals in order not to recognize and enjoy their very real successes.

6. "Don't." This injunction is given by the scared parent: "Don't do anything, because anything you do may lead to disaster."

The child may decide to do, but remain scared in the magic hope that fear or anxiety will ward off the evil eye. Or the person may stay an obsessive through life, avoiding decisions, or may decide not to grow up so that others will decide for him or her.

7. "Don't be important." The child may decide not to be important, thereby not asking for what is needed or wanted, or may decide not to feel important. Oftentimes the decision is not to be important in a particular area or in particular ways. For example, it may be all right to be important on the job but not at home, or vice versa.

8. "Don't belong." This may be a family decision, which a child may adopt, saying: "We don't belong in this community, we only belong to each other," or it may be an individual child's decision with the result that the child feels self to be different from the family. Boys pick a favorite story such as "The Lone Ranger," who belongs nowhere.

9. "Don't be close," or "Don't trust," or "Don't love." This injunction may be given by parents who are not physically close, or who push a child aside. It is also given by the accident of death, or by separation. The child may decide, "I'll never again care about men, because they die," or "I'll do everything for myself," or, "When I grow up I won't get married," or, "I'll never trust a woman again," etc.

10. "Don't be well," or "Don't be sane." Example: One family we treated consisted of a paranoid father, a depressed and suicidal mother, and a daughter diagnosed as schizophrenic. Father would become overtly paranoid,

mother would threaten suicide, then daughter would do something sufficiently bizarre to require hospitalization. Father would then rally to her support, mother would stop being depressed, and as soon as the daughter returned to the family, the cycle would begin again. The injunction was: "Don't be sane, because if you are sane we will have to recognize our own insanity," and daughter bought it. Many long-term patients received their most treasured strokes from their parents during bouts of childhood diseases, and decided to be ill to receive strokes. They linger in groups and on couches, continuing to "make progress" but, when in danger of being declared well enough to terminate, they find new symptoms for the therapist to stroke.

In addition to these "behavior injunctions," we list injunctions against thinking: "Don't think" (which is similar to "Don't grow"), "Don't think about X" (sex, mechanical things, etc.); "Don't think what you think, think what I think." We also list feeling injunctions: "Don't feel" (similar to "Don't be close"), "Don't feel X" (particular feelings), and "Don't feel what you feel, feel what I feel" ("I'm cold, put on your sweater.") Again, children accept, reject, and modify these injunctions.

Redecisions

Years ago Eric Berne said, "As I get ready to go into a group, I think about how I can cure each person in there in one session." This statement agreed with what we had been thinking--we take too long in psychotherapy. How could we speed the change, facilitate faster? We disliked long statistical papers listing which patients could not be cured or treated. It seemed to us that the problem was in the therapy and the therapists, not in the patients. Thus our hunger for new ways of treating was partially abated by Eric, and partially by Fritz Perls, as we kept looking for better and better ways of facilitating change. Then as we learned to use a combination of TA/gestalt/ behavior modification (stroke giving and receiving) plus whatever else we could dream up, and using those combinations in weekend, weeklong, monthlong training, we began to see patients changing without months or years of therapy or analysis.

At about the same time that we were looking at the decisions made by patients when children, we began to realize that if the child made a decision, he could, and often did, change it later, and not necessarily in therapy. As we heard his early decision in some gestalt work, when he was in his Child ego state in an early scene, we recognized that we were listening either to what really happened or what he thought happened, and it didn't make any difference. We began to ask him, "What would you rather say?" or, "And now?" and the patient, still in his Child ego state, would shift, change, make a new decision, or restate the old in a way that was now appropriate for this time and this place. Patients began to get in touch with the power they had as little kids to make the decisions necessary for them to exist psychologically if not physically. It is far easier for someone to change from a position of power than from a feeling of weakness; the notion that they had scripts stuck into their heads led patients to feel it was all hopeless; but if they perceive that *they* were the ones to decide to be distant, or sick, or childlike, or always working, then they were the ones who could change all that. Thus the redecision theory was born, from awareness of where patients were and where they were going, on their own steam, their own strength.

Eric used to talk of the despair people felt when they made a decision, or dropped their script, or stopped playing some major game. Some of this was probably self-fulfilling prophecy if you know that if you change something you are going to despair for a while, then you will probably despair; some of it was due to change in time structure and stroking patterns; some of it, however, was the result of the decision being made in the Adult, instead of the Child. If the Adult deprives the Child of strokes, and his power, by stopping him from playing games, or from getting strokes for rackets, then of course the Child may despair. But if the Child makes the redecision, with the approval of the Adult, then the Child looks for ways of changing his stroking pattern, his time structuring, with considerable enthusiasm. In addition, when he changes, redecides in intensive workshops with us, he gets, immediately, tremendous stroking from a large group of people over an extended period of time. He gets them from his fellow participants, multiple leaders, therapists, cooks, dishwashers, secretaries, gardeners, housekeepers, and even the dogs and horses!

How do we get people into their Child states—or rather how do we facilitate their getting there themselves? By working in the here and now, and not allowing people to talk *about* the past, we facilitate an immediate shift into the Child. For instance, John, in talking about his feeling stupid, said "I had this really terrible teacher in the third grade, who was just awful, and made me feel stupid." (We don't believe that anyone makes anyone else feel anything, of course, but a child doesn't know that.) One of us responds, "Be there, be in the third grade, see your teacher there, and tell her, 'You are a terrible teacher. You won't give me any strokes for my brightness; you don't understand me; you make me feel stupid.' Use little kid words—Be a little kid." John said "When I was in the second grade, the teacher liked me, and smiled at me, but all you do is look nasty, and put me in the back row. You're not fair. Hey, *you're* not fair; it isn't me that's stupid, it is you. I'm not stupid, I am smart. I have a graduate degree now, and I'm not a bit stupid." As he moved back into Adult with the last statement, he grinned a big grin, and began to give up playing "Stupid."

Another way to is to get people to say some particularly important phrase or sentence, originally about their past, in the present, several times. For instance, we could have asked Johnny, if he were not in his Child while talking to the teacher, to say, "You're not fair" several times. In this case, it wasn't necessary.

Another method is in doing gestalt dream work. As people tell their dreams we ask them to tell the story as if they were dreaming it right now, and be all the characters, and all the parts—rooms, doors, walls, cars, etc. As they take on these parts, and describe themselves as the parts, they begin to recognize themselves, often as Adapted Child in one part, Free Child in another, Nurturing and Critical Parents in others. Starting a dialogue between these various parts, often with movement around the room, enables the dreamer to get into his various ego states very quickly. He experiences his Child, his Adult, his Parent, phenomenologically. Dreams are a specially good vehicle for third-degree impasse work.

In brief, we classify impasses, or stuck places, into three degrees: first-degree, between P_2 and A_1; second-degree, between P_1 and A_1; third-degree impasse, between Natural or Free Child and Adapted Child.

The first-degree impasse relates to the drivers or to the counterscript injunctions. For example, most therapists probably received the message, "Work hard," as most of us do. In order to stop working as hard, it is not sufficient simply to decide not to, from A_2. It is important to get into an early scene, when father or mother is giving the message in some remembered way, and to then answer from the Child ego state, as with, "I am not going to work so damned hard anymore just to get strokes; I'm going to take it easy and work just for me, not for you." Sometimes this decision is accompanied by a nonverbal gesture.

The second-degree impasse relates to an injunction and an early decision such as, "Mother said, 'Sometimes I wish I had never had you'" [Don't be], and the child says inside his head, "Someday I'll kill myself, and then you'll be sorry you said that." In the relived scene he may say, "Don't blame me for being here; you and Dad fucked, that's how I got here; it's not my fault, and I refuse to take the blame anymore. I'm living, enjoying life, and I'll be damned if I'll accept the blame for your sadness," thus breaking through the impasse, and deciding to live from now on.

We don't draw the third-degree impasse in structural diagrams, but in functional ones. Some people like to draw it in between C_1 and A_1, but I see it differently. The Little Professor (A_1) decided to go along in order to get along, but he also wants to be free, so the struggle is between those two parts, the Adapted and the Free Child. Such impasses relate to adaptation so early, or so pre-verbal, that the patient seldom recognizes that it is an adaptation; he experiences that he has *always* been clumsy, or *always* been worthless, or *always* felt like the other sex. Thus while the first- and second-degree impasses are I-Thou dialogues, the third-degree impasses are worked through in I-I dialogues, as "I have always felt worthless, I shouldn't be allowed to live" and then, "Hey, I have survived some pretty tough times, and I am still here, and I'm really a neat guy." Several moves back and forth end in the patient usually giving up the adaptation, as he first claims one side, then the other.

Some research has now been done on the work that we do (Lieberman, Yalom, & Miles, 1973; McNeel, 1975), and the reports are positive.

17   *Phobias*

D uring my second year field work for my MSW I was assigned a phobic patient and then warned, "Never tackle a phobia directly, or it may go underground and proliferate." Since this sounded ominous I certainly did not tackle his phobia, and he left as phobic as he'd entered. I hate failing, and have spent the last few years perfecting my treatment of phobias.

Bob Goulding and I use the following methods to promote Child redecisions:

1) TA/gestalt reworking of old scenes
2) Desensitization (Wolpe, 1974)
3) The gestalt technique of being the feared object and claiming the projections
4) Any combination of the above, and
5) Any of the above plus teaching needed skills, such as curing water phobics while teaching them to swim.

Who are phobics? Unfortunately most of the literature is esoteric, unhelpful, and insulting to the phobic. Phobics are any of us who are afraid of something that probably isn't harmful (planes and cars sometimes are), and certainly isn't harming us right now. In spite of the lit-

---

First appeared in somewhat different form in *Transactional Analysis Journal*, 1977, 1(1), 44-54.

erature calling phobics passive—dependent and manipulative, I find them to be no more so than the population at large. In fact, phobics are the population at large.

There are 38 therapists in our current four-week workshop. Today I lectured on phobias and afterwards asked how many are phobic. Seventeen raised their hands. I then asked how many are phobic and pretend they are not, by telling themselves, "I just don't like this or that." Another six raised their hands. Some of them have kept themselves from being as important as they might be, by being afraid to give speeches in public. Most, however, use their phobias to curtail their fun. They don't permit themselves full sexual enjoyment, or the fun of swimming, walking in woods, riding roller coasters, or climbing heights.

Some phobics do use their phobias to manipulate others. Women in our culture get men to empty mousetraps by being afraid of mice. A client of ours who had not gone out of his house alone in years, did, of course, keep his family with him. However, when he was no longer phobic, he was delighted not to have them around all the time.

Why are some people phobic? We have found that phobias are Child decisions made to protect oneself, usually at an age when the child believed in magic. However, in response to a new trauma, a Child of any age may become phobic. A counterphobic parachutist developed a severe plane phobia after a jumping accident. A depressed woman developed a car phobia. Because phobias are Child decisions, I prefer to classify them according to injunctions.

"Don't Be"

The phobias in response to "Don't be" injunctions and decisions are usually of heights, water, diving, flying, ferris wheels, roller coasters, ski lifts, and being alone. Sometimes the fear of crowded spaces and elevators and closed rooms are in response to "Don't be" but more often they are responses to "Don't trust.".

1. A child receiving this injunction may decide to commit suicide, "and then they'll be sorry," but then become so panicky with the decision that she will set up phobias to protect herself.

2. A child may survive a situation seen as potentially lethal, such as a swimming accident, and decide never to go near water again. In this case, there may not have been a "Don't be" injunction, except for that "given" by the situation, and the Child may not have made a decision to die.

3. A child may be frightened for her life and not be able to protect herself, and decide to displace the fear onto something more controllable. A woman whose father died suddenly of pneumonia when she was young transferred all her fears of death to a fear of planes; she would not fly, and therefore felt safe.

An example:
Therapist (Mary): "Whatcha see?"
Client (Carrie): "Cows."
Mary: "What?"
Carrie: "Cows. I was going to take a walk out there, and then I saw the cows. And I do want to walk around your property but I can't . . ."
Mary: "Won't."
Carrie: "I won't as long as there are cows."
(She tells about a frightening incident with a cow that had been shot and wounded. I try to set up a desensiti-

zation, but she remains anxious about what the cows might do. I ask her to scare the others in the group by telling them wild stories about cows; she does, and feels better.)

Mary: "OK. Now are you willing to pick out a cow up there on the hillside and talk to her? Tell her how close you will come to her."

Carrie: "It's—it's not just the shooting. There may be a bull up there I can't see, an injured one somewhere, or a calf I can't see, and I might accidentally do something the cow doesn't like, like get between the mother and the calf."

Mary: "Tell the cow that the world is full of a million scares, and you have to stay on top of them."

Carrie: "Yea, that's it. That ties into some old stuff."

Mary: "You have to have everything worked out."

Carrie: "That's exactly where it is."

Mary: "OK, I'm going to give you a fantasy I wouldn't usually give, but I think you can handle it. Will you pretend that you have accidentally walked between the cow and her calf. You are there, and the cow starts to move toward you. And now imagine that you bellow 'Boo' as loud as you can bellow. And now have the cow start to bawl, because cows are the biggest sissies in the world. Pretend that you have plenty of time to move away."

Following this work, Carrie walked easily near the cows—and so did I. I'd cured my phobia while treating her.

All of these phobic decisions are "pro-life." Later, however, the person may use them to justify suicide. The person afraid to go out of his or her home may say, "I might as well be dead as live like this."

"Don't"

The injunction "Don't" is given by phobic parents; if the Child decides to accept, he or she also accepts the phobia.

An example:

Betty: "Can I work on a bridge? I'd like to give up a bridge phobia."

Mary: "Sure. Got a particular bridge?"

(Betty describes the bridge near her home and her panic when driving over it.)

Mary: "OK. So will you be willing to start driving? Put your hands on the steering wheel. Get the feeling of being in your car. OK?"

Betty: "OK."

Mary: "Drive to where the bridge starts."

Betty: "I'm there."

Mary: "Get out of the car and look over the edge. OK?"

Betty: "OK."

Mary: "Will you test out saying, 'I'm not going to jump off the bridge, and I'm not going to drive my car off the bridge'?"

Betty: "I'm not going to jump off you, and I'm not going to drive off you."

Mary: "True?"

Betty: "True. Definitely." *(Slowly, we continue, stopping each time she is anxious, until she is almost to the crest of the bridge, where she is particularly anxious.)*

Mary: "Get out and look over the railing and say, 'I'm not going to jump off or drive off.'"

Betty: "I am not going to jump off or drive off. I AM NOT."

Mary: "Do you feel OK standing there?"

Betty: "Yes; uh huh." *(I ask Betty to describe what she sees, to get her to enjoy the scene. She does.)*

Mary: "Now will you see your parents way down there below you on the edge of the river?"

Betty: "OK. I see them."

Mary: "Tell them about jumping or driving off."

Betty: "Yes. Hey, I can drive over this bridge without going off it."

Mary: "What does your mother say?"

Betty: "Be careful." *(Laughs a "recognition" laugh.)* "My Daddy says, 'Sure.'"

Mary: "Say some more to your mother."

Betty: "Look, Mother, I've never driven off before, and I'm not driving off now. And you're telling me to be careful doesn't help."

Mary: "What are you feeling?"

Betty: "I feel calm."

Mary: "OK, would you put your mother in the car with you?"

Betty: "Oh, Jesus. NO! That's the problem. I'm taking her out."

Mary: "Want to drive further?"

Betty: "I am driving. Wow, for the first time I am not tense. This is wonderful. I am slowing down at the top. I can just relax and look out at the view. I feel fine."

Mary: "Great. And if you ever scare yourself again, will you tell your mother in your head that you are competent, whether she knows it or not?"

Betty: "I sure will."

Persons with multiple phobias were often raised by panphobic parents. If everything the child thinks of doing is called dangerous by a terrified parent, the child has a hard time learning to cope, and therefore uses phobias to avoid, rather than Adult functioning to assess, situations.

"Don't Be Close" or "Don't Be Sexual"

A woman who was phobic of dancing redecided that it was all right to be close to men. After her fine work, we asked her if she was ready to be desensitized. She laughed, said, "I am desensitized," picked a partner from the group, and danced. Her phobia had been designed to support her Child decision about closeness and sexuality.

There are many specific sexual phobias, and often orgasmic difficulties are caused by one's own or one's partner's phobias. When women do not have orgasms, for example, either the woman or her partner may be phobic about some aspects of foreplay.

Also, as Freud knew, sexual phobias may be projected. We worked once with a person who was afraid of cats. We asked her to be a cat and describe herself. She was amazed to discover that what she defined as a cat was a lithe, beautiful, seductive, and sexual being! She claimed these attributes and dropped her phobia. As is often the case, her phobia was a remnant from a childhood decision. As an adolescent she redecided about sex and had no difficulties being a beautiful sexual being.

"Don't Trust"

People who decide not to trust may be phobic in any situation where their lives are literally in someone else's hands. This seems to be the basic component of fear of flying, or riding in a car, or taking an elevator. All of the fears listed under the "Don't be" injunction apply to the nontrusting person if the fear is of being killed, rather than of killing oneself. (Usually, those who decide not to trust have a primary "Don't be" injunction.) Fear of the dark is a fear of those creatures out there, hidden by the darkness. The fear may be a projection of the Child's own self-destructive decisions, or may be a fear based on Child information that the world contains people who "want" to kill her (doctors who take out tonsils, cruel parents or teachers). Often the "cause" is buried in the past and does not need to be dealt with.

Jay: "I want to stop being afraid of the dark." *(He describes his fear as minor, a "creepy" feeling, and recalls an intense fear as a child after seeing "The Wizard of Oz.")*

Mary: "How did your parents react?"

Jay: "I don't remember."

Mary: "I bet I know what they didn't do. I bet they didn't give you a flashlight."

Jay: "No they didn't." *(Jay lives alone. We set up the scene in his present home, and he explored his darkened house, turning on his imaginary flashlight whenever he was anxious. When he was afraid, for example, to open the door to the cellar, I asked him to call out, "I'm scared to open you, because the Wicked Witch may be down there." He enjoyed this and began laughing as he realized that the witch is no match for his strong, six-foot-three, present self.)*

Jay: "So I open the door. You don't scare me, Wicked Witch. I turn off my flashlight—and I run like hell." *(Gallows laughter from group.)*

Mary: "Wait—that's not going to help you any."

Jay: "Nope."

Mary: "Turn your light on again. What do you see?" *(He describes and explores the basement and says he is calm again.)*

Mary: "OK. Turn off your flashlight. What do you see?"

Jay: "Blackness. I see the window on the north wall."

Mary: "Blackness has many colors and textures. Look carefully."

Jay: "The windows have a lighter tone. In the northeast corner it is very dark. [*He continues to get in touch with colors and textures.*] The branches against the window are beautiful."

Mary: "Are you ready to walk back into your bedroom?"

Jay: "Yeah."

Mary: "Want your flashlight on or off?"

Jay: "I want to do it with the flashlight off. I am walking down the hall. [*Pause*] As I walk, I feel this little shiver down my spine."

Mary: "Will you enjoy that? Feel your shiver just for a moment as a little sexy shiver."

Jay: "Yeah, OK. Yeah, it is. Down my back and down my sides. Whew. I like that. I want to run and jump in bed and enjoy my shiver. Yeah, right now, I feel a lot of movement in my body. I am in bed." (*He goes on to enjoy the lighter and darker aspects of his own room and his own body. Then he says he is fine, and we finish.*)

Group Member: "Did you have a domineering mother?"

Other Group Member: "Wouldn't it be better to explore the meaning of the witch?"

Mary: "It doesn't matter what the witch represented. That was a long time ago, so don't fuck around with his exwitch."

"Don't Be Important"

In all public-speaking phobias I have found a decision not to be important, not to "go public" again. Most often, the decision was made the first time the Child, full of excitement and self-importance, was shamed or ridiculed by parents, peers, or teachers.

"Don't Be The Sex You Are"

We cured two men of phobias they considered to be "fears only women have"—snake and mice phobias. I do not know that their phobias were related to their early sexual identity confusions; however, they used their phobias to harass themselves for not being "sufficiently" male. One woman, who was supposed to be a boy, was an excellent baseball player until adolescence, when she developed such an intense fear of the ball that she stopped playing. This phobia seemingly was in the service of her becoming what she thought of as "more female."

"Don't Make It"

Sometimes a phobic decision prevents a person from being successful. One client would not give up his plane phobia in spite of desensitization, until he decided not to be president of his firm. When he resigned, he took his family on a plane trip to a resort. This was his first plane trip in 20 years (except for one trial in a small plane after his first desensitization), and he enjoyed it.

Whenever a person uses a phobia to keep herself from being successful, I also look for other aspects of a "Don't make it" decision. Fear of streets, high buildings, bridges, flying, or driving may be used to keep the person from advancing professionally.

"Don't Have Fun"

Many successful therapists decided early not to have fun: to work rather than play. Otherwise, how would we have forced ourselves to get "A" marks in uninteresting courses, year after year? It is more than coincidental that most phobic therapists have phobias that limit their fun.

"Don't Grow"

All phobias that involve someone else having to do something because the person won't do it herself reinforce a decision not to grow. This does not mean such people are passive-dependent; it simply means that in a particular way the person has used fear to limit her independence. Such a person may rid her house of mice by independently contracting with an exterminating company, or she may in this area remain dependent on a nonphobic spouse.

Cultural conditioning supports insect, rodent, and reptile phobias in women. Little girls are loved, comforted, held and called "cute" when they are afraid, whereas boys are shamed, ridiculed, even punished. Further, should a little girl bring one of these creatures into the house, she may well witness mother screaming and father taking charge. We find more women than men who say they are afraid of small creatures. In other areas, men and women seem to be equally phobic.

Treatment

Because phobias are based on Child decisions, cure consists of a Child redecision that "I am not afraid!" Our goal, then, is for the participant to experience *without fear* that which was previously feared.

Bob and I treat all participants in group, both because doing so is economical (in terms of our time and effort and clients' money) and because group support and encouragement are an integral part of our approach. Though we almost always work together, we find that in desensitization—as in dream work—two therapists are distracting, so one or the other sits back, coming in only if something important has been overlooked. We never work more than 30 minutes with a patient and usually cure phobias

in about 15 minutes. If the participant is extremely phobic, or if we and the participant haven't found the right
"key," we may work up to 30 minutes on two or three
consecutive days. When a participant contracts to cease
being phobic, we first make certain that she has "closed
the escape hatches" (as Harry Boyd says). If the person
is in any degree suicidal, homicidal, or psychotic, work
in these areas takes precedence. Any person who is using
a phobia to collect stamps for suicide must decide, "I
won't kill myself even if I never get rid of my phobia"
before I will work with her to drop her phobia. Next, I'll
ask for the details of a phobia to make sure that what the
person wants to do is, in fact, safe. (It is not phobic to be
afraid to dive to depths where any error could mean
death.) I ask about advantages and disadvantages of the
phobia and about who will be affected by the participant's
cure. Finally, I want the client to clear up any unrealistic
expectations. Learning to swim or to enjoy sex will not
necessarily make her spouse love her. Being a good public
speaker will not necessarily lead to self-respect; in fact,
since self-respect is a more important issue than public
speaking, I'd work first on respecting oneself while
phobic.

TA-Gestalt Reworking of Past Scenes

I will use this approach first when the ramifications of
the old decision include more than the phobia. Reworking
an old scene, then, may involve deciding solidly to live,
be close, grow up, and be important. I may also use it
when a participant remembers developing a phobia in
response to a traumatic incident.
Example. A participant learned to be afraid of heights
because his father used to dangle him over a ledge when
he was three to six years old. He went back into the

scene. He became enraged at Father and told him, "You are a bastard—a bully—a little nothing man—a cheap nothing. You can't prove you're a man with other men, so you mess with me—I'd like to beat you—I hate you." When he had finished with his anger, he felt sad, a feeling he had not previously allowed himself to feel towards his father. "I'm sorry for you. You always felt so inferior. You really were inferior in ways." He cried. Then, several minutes later, he laughed, "You know what, you bastard, you weren't trying to kill me like I thought. If you had decided to kill me, you'd have dropped me. I was not in danger. And I'm not in danger now." He came back to the present. "Shit, I'm a foot taller than my father. Nobody's going to dangle me like that. I take care of myself fine." When he was finished, he hiked up our road on the cliff side. That weekend he had a good time walking safely and enthusiastically near the cliffs at Point Lobos State Park.

Desensitization

Wolpe (1969) uses the parental philosophy, "Calm down." He teaches participants relaxation techniques prior to desensitization. We prefer Fritz Perls' philosophy that excitement is the best replacement for anxiety. Sometimes we use the classical approach of having the person sit, keeping hands visible to the therapist. The person is then instructed to raise the left forefinger when uncomfortable and the right forefinger when comfortable. Beginning where the participant is least anxious, he or she is led on a fantasy trip, or is told to act out the scene.

Lupe: "I am scared since I am a little girl. I have always been scared about the little animals—spiders, cucarachas, all kinds of little animals. And since I live in _____ there are a lot of little animals."

Mary: "OK, so you see an insect, and what do you do?"

Lupe: "I scream and someone kills." *(Giggles. I might have gone with her giggle, asking how old she is while giggling, and taken her back to that time, in order to work with an early scene. I decided to stay in the present instead.)*

Mary: "What would you rather do?"

Lupe: "I'd rather kill that animal."

Mary: "Why? You have a fine system. You scream, others kill." *(Lupe explains that she is teaching the autonomy of women throughout South America, and she considers phobias to be nonautonomous.)*

Mary: "OK. Let's pretend. Let's start with a small one. Ant. You know *ant*?"

Lupe: "Yes."

Mary: "OK. There's a little ant on the floor right there. Just a little, tiny, tiny one."

Lupe: "I can do that."

Mary: "Go ahead."

Lupe: *(Gets up and steps on the ant, squashing it with her shoe.)*

Mary: "What do you feel?"

Lupe: "OK. No, I don't like to kill him."

Mary: "How come?"

Lupe: "I don't like to hurt that little animal."

Mary: "OK. See another ant. Say to it, 'My house is your house. You may stay in my house and bring all your brothers and sisters and cousins.'"

Lupe: "No. No. If it is one ant, I am with a [*gestures sweeping*]."

Group: "Broom."

Lupe: "Yes, I do this." *(Pretends to sweep the imaginary ant out the door, opens door and sweeps it out.)*

Mary: "OK?"

Lupe: "OK!"

Mary: "Now see a cockroach—cucaracha—over there. OK?"

Lupe: "Yes."

Mary: "First tell it what you want. In the house or out of the house?"

Lupe: "Out of the house."

Mary: "Tell it what you are going to do."

Lupe: "Well, what I do is [*pause*]. I call for somebody. No, I don't want to call for somebody. [*Pause.*]"

Mary: "So tell it what you are going to do."

Lupe: "I am going to bring the—what is the name?"

Group: "Broom."

Lupe: "Broom. Broom. I am going to bring the broom. 'Out of my house!' [*She sweeps.*] I open the door. [*She sweeps it outside.*]"

Mary: "OK. You OK?"

Lupe: "Yes."

Mary: "Ready for a spider?"

Lupe: "Yes."

Mary: "OK, see it and tell it." *(She sweeps.)*

Mary: "What are you thinking?"

Lupe: "They are going to come."

Mary: "Sure, they are going to come back in. Are you going to keep sweeping them out?"

Lupe: *(Laughs joyously.)* "No, I am not. I am too tired." *(She stamps happily around the room, squashing bugs, as the group cheers and applauds.)*

Three rules are followed while using desensitization:

1. Never, at any time, force a phobic patient. Set up the fantasy, or let the participant set it up, and then never move faster than the participant—without fear—is willing to move.

2. Do not let the patient believe "I can't," or "The [feared object] scared me." Instead, ask the participant to recognize the truth: "I don't do what I am afraid to do," and "I am afraid of insects," or even, "I scare myself about insects."

3. The participant needs to reinforce a fantasy desensitization with a reality experience as soon as possible after the desensitization.

Being the Feared Object

Just after Lupe had finished her work, another woman brought up her fear of spiders. She was specifically afraid that they would crawl on her. I had her be the spider, crawl on her arm, and accept the qualities she attributed to the spider: inquisitiveness, excitement, and fear of being too little to protect herself. That was all the work I did with her because she had already "piggybacked" on Lupe's work. During the break, the two women hunted spiders on our property, let them crawl on their hands, and killed them.

Combined Techniques

Mary: "Why do you want to give up fear of snakes?"

Annie tells of not going on vacations, running out of the room if snakes are mentioned, etc. She is obviously frightened while talking. We discuss snakes, including the positive aspects of knowing which are and aren't harmful. I then begin a brief, unsatisfactory desensitizing scene using a movie on TV of a tiny garter snake. She does not get comfortable. She will not fantasize a live snake at any distance. She then describes her fear that a snake would crawl all over her, she being unable to protect herself because she wouldn't dare touch it. She claimed her only recourse would be to faint.)

Mary: "Does that fit anything in your life? It's a kinda far-out fantasy—you can't, or won't, protect and won't touch, so your only recourse is to faint."

Annie: "No. I can't click into anything." (*I decide not to push in that direction. I have no treatment contract with this woman, except to work with her to cure her phobia. She is a participant in a partner's workshop.*)

Mary: "OK, then. I want you to pretend, without prejudice, that you are a snake, a lovely king snake. [*I describe a king snake.*] Will you be a you be a king snake and be way out there under the redwood trees? Right now?"

Annie: "I am black and white. It's hard for me to think of a snake as lovely."

Mary: "OK."

Annie: "I am black and white and . . . slithery. And I . . . I move really fast. And I make a rustling noise." (*Pause.*)

Mary: "What do you feel as you move? What sensations?"

Annie: "I feel—I feel someone is walking by and I want them to go away." (*This is not the proper occasion to deal with the difference between "think" and "feel".*)

Mary: "Will you tell the person that?"

Annie: "I am scared of you. I don't want to wrap around you."

Mary: "In fact, I've never in my life wrapped around a person?"

Annie: "No, I've never wrapped around a person. 'Cause I don't let people get that close to me."

Mary: "Now be you and respond."

Annie: "I am glad you are going away. You are just as scared of me as I am of you."

Mary: "Be the snake again. Anything else about being the snake?"

Annie: "I like to lie out in the sun and sleep and I move the way I do because it is the only way I know how to move. I enjoy moving that way. I enjoy the feel of the grass when I slither through it. It's really nice. A sensual movement."

Mary: "I am nice and I move sensually. Will you claim that for you?"

Annie: *(Laughs.)* "Yes, yes. I like that feeling and I identify with that feeling. That wiggling. That kind of movement."

Mary: "OK. Come here [*I take her to the closed glass doors.*] Are you willing to see that black and white king snake slithering way down there in the grass."

Annie: "MMMhmmm."

Mary: "Let it come as close as you are willing without being at all afraid."

Annie: *(Looks out; doesn't appear afraid.)*

Mary: "Where is it?"

Annie: "Right there at that bare patch [*about 20 feet away*]."

Mary: "You feel OK?"

Annie: "Yes."

Mary: "Fine. That's enough for today. You've come a long way."

Annie: "Yes, I have. Thank you very much."

Mary: "I'll be glad to find time tomorrow or Monday to work again. In the meantime, start reading about snakes. OK?"

Annie: "OK."

A participant may start with desensitization and then remember an early scene:

Mary: "What are you afraid of?"

Shirley: "I'm afraid the car will go over the edge."

Mary: "Are you willing to say 'I am afraid I will drive the car over the edge'?"

Shirley: "I wouldn't drive the car over the edge. I'm not suicidal."

Mary: "You know how to drive?"

Shirley: "Sure."

Mary: "Good driver?"

Shirley: "Sure."

Mary: "Then the car can't go over the edge. Either you drive it over or you don't."

Shirley: "I guess that's true."

Mary: "That's true."

(Then I ask her to start driving, stop when anxious, etc.) Suddenly she said, "This is all from when I was a kid." *(We stopped the desensitization, and I asked her to go back to the scene she was remembering):* "I am in the back seat of my parents' car, and they are quarreling about my father's driving. The more Mother pleads and screams, the worse he drives, and I am terrified."

(As she works on this scene, she realizes for the first time that Father was not a dangerous driver, never had an accident in his entire life, and that the problem was their quarrels and Mother's phobia. Then Shirley remembers her impulse to open the car door and jump out, to punish them for fighting and not paying attention to her. Now Shirley is ready to get back in her own car.)

Shirley: "I am not throwing myself out of my car, I am not driving dangerously, I have never driven dangerously. I am in charge of my car and I drive it well." *(That afternoon she drove on a nearby mountainous road easily, and is no longer phobic.)*

In treating participants for their fears of public speaking, I use a variety of approaches. First, I ask for catastrophic expectations. "If you should agree to give that lecture, what is the worst thing that could happen?" "What happens next?" "Next?" "And how would you handle this?" I continue questioning until the person recognizes she will cope. I may then use the "Be the feared object" approach and ask that participant to be the audience. She easily identifies that the punitive, derisive audience is in reality her own Critical Parent. The next step may be to fight back decisively in the Child ego state, and that is best in an early scene. The early scene is most often cited as reading aloud, or reciting when young, and feeling ashamed. In reworking the scene, she will need to realize that the persecutor back then was at fault, and that it is OK for a person to make a mistake. The driver-injunction complex behind this phobia is, "Be perfect— Don't make it."

After the Child has redecided, it will then be appropriate to desensitize in a fantasied future scene where the participant is giving a public speech. I ask that she begin to speak to an audience of one and increase the number slowly as she feels comfortable (or excited).

Combining Techniques With Teaching

In almost every workshop, Bob Goulding has participants cure themselves of being afraid of the water, of putting their heads under, of keeping their eyes open, of floating on their backs, of swimming in deep water, or of diving. Using the above-mentioned techniques, he also teaches the skills. Most kids who are poor in sports are phobic. Unfortunately, the usual teaching methods accentuate negative stroking while teaching skills that won't be learned by a phobic youngster. Such children, (and grown-ups, too) may become acceptable athletes, or at least enjoy the sport, when they are desensitized of their fears, taught needed skills, and stroked positively for each gain.

In all our work we look for ways to make treating both fun and beautiful for the therapists, the participants, and the whole group. As in the work with Jay, a Child with a flashlight can solve most problems. Our work is based on providing flashlights.

18   Monogamy: An Answer to "Rapo"   —M.M.G.

M any modern therapists advocate sexually open mar-
riages. We find that the open marriage is an invitation to games, and is usually practiced to live out "Don't
trust" injunctions to further an unhappy script. In the following clinical example, the woman and her husband, recently married, had not yet been hurt by their nonmonogamous contract. As in all cases when a suspected game
has not yet been played out, we asked her to play it in
fantasy, and then make the redecisions necessary so that
she would not play it in reality.

Chelo: "I'd like to work. My contract is—I must—I
want to stop my feelings of jealousy at my husband. I
make myself feel jealous. Not so much as before. I still
make myself feel jealous at times, feel very bad, and I
don't like it."

Mary: "Get in touch with your body right now. Your
posture."

Chelo: "Yes?"

Mary: "What do you experience?"

Chelo: "I am closed up, tight. I do not let me relax. I
do not permit comfort. [Stretches.] Now, I'm comfortable
and ready to work."

Bob: "What do you mean by jealousy?"

Chelo: "I mean, if I see him flirting with another woman, I feel jealous, hurt. I change that very quickly to anger and then I make a wall. I stay angry and then I want to hurt him."

Bob: "Do you and he have a monogamous sexual contract? That you do not fuck anyone else?"

Chelo: "We do not. We do not make a rigid rule because we do not want to be rigid. We want a flexible relationship."

Bob: "That's the setup for jealousy."

Chelo: "But I'd rather learn not to be jealous. Not a monogamous contract. I had that before and it was no good. My exhusband and I didn't keep it."

Mary: "At what point is it all right to be jealous? You said you didn't want to be jealous when you see him flirting. How about screwing?"

Chelo: "He doesn't do that. But it should be all right if he does."

(Now it is obvious that we have a Parental contract. She "wants" to change something she thinks she should change, in order to be a good girl in this modern world.)

Chelo: "I would want to work on accepting it, if he did what you say."

Bob: "I am not willing to work with this contract."

Mary: "Neither am I. Your contract is how to have drama instead of intimacy."

(We worked with Chelo two years ago, in a marathon, when she was both hysterical and suicidal. The drama of her first marriage involved third-degree, tissue-damaging games. At this time, though still overly dramatic, she held a good job, was not suicidal, and had a better marriage than previously.)

Chelo: "I see myself having to stop jealousy. Even if we had what you call a monogamous contract I do not see myself stopping being jealous."

Bob: "So, pretend you have a monogamous contract. How do you become jealous?"

Chelo: "I would find ways not to believe him. I would not believe him even though I know he is a fine person. He would like a monogamous contract."

Bob: "So, where you are stuck is you were taught not to trust."

Chelo: "True, Very true. My mother says don't ever trust a man. And my father didn't like me. He rejected me. And mother says that is the way with men."

Mary: "So the way to live out those messages is simple. You either pick an untrustworthy guy, or you pick a trustworthy guy and set up a contract about sex—about sex that will end up with the guy proving he is untrustworthy. That's what your nonmonogamous contract is—a way to prove your mother was right. Please don't be faithful so that I can feel toward you the way mother felt toward father."

Chelo: "I think I understand. That is interesting. If I tell him it is all right whatever he does with another woman, then I am telling him to be like my father? My father was never faithful to my mother. Yes, I understand."

Bob: "A nonmonogamous contract is a game contract, where one or both is supposed to end up feeling bad. For instance, pretend for a moment that your husband finds another woman to screw. You find out. Someone tells you. What do you feel?"

Chelo: "Jealous."

Bob: "And what do you say to yourself about him?"

Chelo: "He is no good. He is—he deceived me."

Bob: "And what do you say about yourself."

Chelo: *(Starts to cry.)* "I am sad. No one will ever love me. I am ugly."

Bob: "Say it again, to yourself. 'He is no good, he deceives me, no one will ever love me, I am ugly.' [*Pause*] How old are you?"

Chelo: "Seven."

Bob: "What is happening? Be there."

(We see the following characteristics in this game:

1. The game begins with an ostensibly straight message: "We want a flexible relationship."

2. With the seemingly straight message, there is a secret message: "Prove you are untrustworthy."

3. There is a response to the secret message: In this case, because the game had not terminated, we asked Chelo to imagine the game termination, which would come when her husband took a lover, for example.

4. Following the real or fantasied response, the player receives the payoff, which includes an unpleasant, hurting feeling plus a statement that the person makes about self and other. These statements represent the confirming of the player's existential position, and come from a past, unclosed gestalt: "I am jealous. He is no good. He deceived me. I am sad. No one will ever love me. I am ugly."

5. The moves of the game are not within Adult awareness.

The most beneficial method of working with any game is to ask the client for the payoff, and then trace the payoff to an early scene.)

Chelo: "My brother is born. I have a confusion about which part I will be working. I have my father rejecting, and I hear my mother saying, 'Don't trust men. They will only hurt you,' and my brother is born and everyone stops paying attention to me. They are all busy with my brother."

Bob: "See your father and talk to him."

Chelo: "You would not touch me. And when I wanted

to talk to you, you were always busy. Always busy. You look down on me. [*Weeps.*] You push me away with your eyes. I hate you—you are an ugly, ugly, ugly man. You look very ugly. I hate you. [*Sobbing.*] I'd like to hit you in the face and break you. You make fun of me. You taught me that I am too dark and I didn't belong in the family. I hate you. I don't want your love. You are incompetent. I am better than you are. You think you are smart. You are stupid. Incompetent." (*Sobs for several minutes.*)

(*In this piece of work Chelo expresses the "Don't be," "Don't belong," and "Don't be close" injunctions. With her decision not to trust, she also seemingly decided that she was inferior, and too dark, and that she would compensate by proving she is "Better [smarter] than you are." She also decided to be sad, angry, and jealous.*

I chose to tackle, first, the decision that she is inferior and unlikeable, but Chelo wouldn't go in that direction.)

Mary: "Stay seven. Get in touch with you as seven. OK? Now tell your father what he missed by not appreciating you."

Chelo: "I don't know. [*Sobs again*] You are selfish. You are not so important. Incompetent. Worth nothing. My brother, I love you. It wasn't your fault. You were beautiful."

(*Here we see the "Don't think" injunction, with her decision, "I don't know." Although she decided to be smarter than father, and educated herself far beyond most women of her background, she often hysterically shut off her thinking. Therefore, Bob asked an Adult question, one of fact.*)

Bob: "Your brother *was* beautiful? Why 'was'?"

Chelo: "I haven't seen him in a long time, since I grew up and left my country."

Bob: "Was he trustworthy?"

Chelo: "I think so. He was very cuddly."

Mary: "And when you were seven, I bet you had other opinions."

Chelo: "When I was seven I thought—he was a spoiled brat."

Mary: "So, from your seven-year-old position, what you do with a husband is wait and expect to be rejected."

Chelo: "Yes, I do wait. I expect someday everyone will reject me."

Mary: "As if they were all your father."

Chelo: "Yes. I do not want to be this way. They are not all like my father. I'd like to tell my mother that there are some men who are trustworthy."

Mary: "OK. Bring another chair."

Chelo: *(Brings chair for mother.)* "Mother, there must be some men who are trustworthy. It is not logical to think that all men are untrustworthy. This is not for us intelligent people to say this. Just imagine if somebody says, 'All women are untrustworthy.' Would you believe that?"

Bob: "Tell her you know one."

Chelo: "Please?"

Bob: "You know one trustworthy man. Me."

Chelo: "You?"

Bob: "Yes, me. I'm trustworthy."

Chelo: "Oh. Yes. I think you are. I know four! [*Group laughter.*] Mother, I know four trustworthy men. And I think you made yourself hurt. You didn't know many things. You didn't know transactional analysis. I do love you very much, but I am not going to accept all your advice. I have my own mind, too. And furthermore, I have met people more intelligent than you. And some of them are trustworthy, and some of them have trust. I am finished."

(This is an example of the way a redecision is made. Chelo has in spirit returned to the home of her youth, the

home she has not seen since she was about 18, and she is talking to her mother, who actually has been out of her life for about 12 years. Going into the scene she brings the facts, the new ideas, the mature sense from all the years since she was seven. Her redecision is made when her Little Professor [A_1] in the Free Child ego state, finding more facts either in that past or in any other time up to and including the present, spontaneously knows a new truth: "I know four trustworthy men." Chelo now has the freedom to begin the exploration of a new trust and closeness.)

The next day Chelo is working on liking herself:

Mary: "Chelo, will you go back to the scene when you are seven, and this time be a grown-up onlooker. See that seven-year-old girl named Chelo, who is very pretty and dark, and needs some grown-up to admire her. OK? See her?"

Chelo: "I see her."

Mary: "Describe the scene."

(Chelo describes her early home, and sees herself as sitting alone outside the kitchen door, while mother is nursing the baby and father is bragging that he finally has a son.)

Mary: "Are you willing to reach out and hold her?"

Chelo: "I think so, She is skinny—she is dark—yes, I reach out and hold you." *(Weeps, as she reaches with her arms and encircles the imagined child, then draws her close.)*

Mary: "Tell her what she needs to know to grow up happy and trusting."

Chelo: "You are very sweet. It is all right to be dark. Some people even like little dark girls. You are smart and you work hard—you are smarter than anyone else in your family will ever be. You are." *(Weeps for several minutes.)*

Bob: "Say to her, 'I love you.'"

Chelo: "I love you." (*Continues to weep, and at the same time she begins to smile.*)

Mary: "Is that true?"

Chelo: "Yes, it is true. I love you. I will take care of you."

Chelo: "I have something to report. Last night I talked to my husband on the telephone. And he is in favor of what we did. He wants a monogamous contract. He says he always wanted a monogamous contract because he doesn't want me loving anyone else but him. [*Group cheers.*] Yes, I am very happy. I am trusting men when they are trustworthy, and he is trustworthy."

Bob: "Great. Now if he flirts, someday, he is just flirting for fun."

Chelo: "Yes, I understand this now. I am satisfied. And I am not jealous. I am not imagining what he is doing. I am not imagining he is flirting. I am saying I am loveable and we are happy."

19   *Redecision: Some Examples*

—*M.M.G.*

In TA literature there are conflicting explanations of the structural and functional theories of the Child ego state. The three-part structural system contains the early, primitive Child (C_1), the Little Professor whose thinking is unprejudiced but limited and distorted (A_1), and the archaic introjects (P_1). The two parts of the functional system are described as Free and Adapted. Within the functional system we see structure. In the Adapted Child, (rebelling or conforming) C_1 pressures are dormant or ignored, P_1 is active, and A_1 decides in response to internal or external Parents. In the Free Child, P_1 pressures are dormant, C_1 is active, and A_1 is free to receive data and make decisions without internal or external Parent pressures.

Decisions in response to real or fantasied injunctions curtail freedom and therefore are made by the Adapted Child. With the adaptation the injunction is locked into P_1 until the person redecides. Early decisions are not thought out logically, of course. We have two mallards on our pond who were raised by awkward, white ducks who couldn't fly higher than eight feet. The grown mallards

---

First appeared in *Transactional Analysis Journal*, 1978, 8(2), 132-135, where its authorship was incorrectly attributed to both Robert L. and Mary M. Goulding.

257

still flop around like white ducks, even though the white ducks are long dead and many pairs of wild mallards have lived with them briefly. In much the same way people flop around in one or another area of life. They usually don't change by getting Adult facts.

Changes by decision of the Adapted Child in response to a therapist's Parent simply gives a new, although perhaps less dangerous, straightjacket. Redecision is made by the Free Child.

The following are examples of redecisions made by the Little Professor in the Free Child ego state:

Peter is a good, quiet, conforming man, not yet a soarer, whose contract goal is to expand the range of feelings he permits himself.

Peter: "I have thought about feelings. There was the occasion when I went to Canada during the war. I was in boarding school and they sent for me. When I reached home my bags were packed. I was being sent from England to Vancouver. I didn't see my parents for six years."

Mary: "Keep it in the present tense. [*In order to help patients get into Child ego states, we encourage them to work in the present tense; otherwise, we are listening to an Adult tell* about *experiences, and the patient doesn't get into a Child state*] Be there at home, before you left for Vancouver. OK?"

Peter: (*Nods.*)

Mary: "How old are you?"

Peter: "I am 13. I don't want to leave."

Mary: "Be there. See your home. Let yourself know your feelings."

Peter: "I don't want to leave. I am also excited. I'm excited about the idea of travel. Canada! I am not worried about dangers. I am in the sitting room. We're having tea. And my mother's there, and my father. And my feeling

changes. I am sad. I am sad at leaving, and at leaving my
friends from boarding school. I'm upset and I nearly cry.
My mother sees me nearly crying and runs out of the
room. My father says, 'You've upset your mother.' I am
terribly ashamed."

Bob: "Be 13, but with what you now know about feelings. Talk to your father."

Peter: "I see mother is upset. We are a close family.
She is about to cry. She's—she's been taught not to cry.
We don't. We are not a very emotional family."

Bob: "That is the understatement of the generations.!"

Peter: "Yes. [*Long pause.*] Perhaps my father wanted
to cry, too." *(Pause.)*

Mary: "Where are you?"

Peter: "I am applying this to other situations in the here
and now."

He did not want to work further. The next day Peter
reported that, following his work, he had walked alone in
the hills and 'cried a bit. Of course, that is not like you
who are willing to cry in public. It may not seem a big
step to you. To me it is a giant step. It is the first time
in my memory that I have cried."

The above example illustrates that redecisions are not
necessarily splashy, and do not all have to occur in the
therapy room. Peter completed his redecision alone in
the hills. If he had been urged or bullied into moving
faster than his own pace, he'd have made the decision
from his Adapted Child, and then perhaps have felt emotionally "raped." (Respect for the patient is the quality
that differentiates "therapist" from "the rapist.")

George's contract goal is to ask without embarrassment
for what he wants. He explores what he wants in his current life, and how he manages not to assert himself to get
it. Then we work with an early scene:

Bob *(getting two chairs):* "In this chair say, 'I'm ashamed.'"

George: "Talking to mother?"

Bob: "No, you aren't talking to mother. Say 'I'm ashamed,' and take that side of you, the ashamed side."

George: "I'm ashamed. I shouldn't ask for—to be nursed. I am too old. I shouldn't ask. I am not good enough. I am too big. I don't need it anymore." *(These, of course, were some of his early decisions made at age three, when his sister was newly born.)*

Bob: "Now sit in the other chair and be the natural kid who asks for a natural thing. Not ashamed. A healthy kid."

George: "I'd like some too, Mother."

Bob: "No, don't talk to Mother. Just be that kid."

George: "I'd like some, too."

Bob: "Say more."

George: "I'd like to be more with the other kids. I'd like to be accepted—"

Mary: "You're getting off the track. Start with 'I'm not ashamed. I am curious.'"

George: "I'm not ashamed. I'm adventuresome. I like to explore. I want to explore the outdoors."

Bob: "I want to explore your tit." *(Whole group laughs.)*

George: *(laughing):* "Yeah. 'I want to explore that tit.' Sure. That fits. Hmmmmm."

Mary: "Any more you need to do?"

George *(still laughing):* "I'm not ashamed, I'll be a great explorer of tits, unashamedly." *(Group applauds.)*

After this session he began practicing his redecision, by asking unapologetically for what he wanted. He got artichokes, spare ribs, and chocolate cake from the chef for dinner. For some people a redecision is so strongly felt that they change almost spontaneously. For others, a period of practice and reinforcement in ongoing groups is necessary.

The following example shows how difficult it is to keep participants from overadaptation and the consequent loss of the opportunity to make Free Child redecisions:

Ann: "I need to be told when I'm discounting my abilities. Could I have a contract with the group that whenever anyone hears me discounting—"

Mary: "Nope."

Ann: "What?"

Mary: "No way."

Ann: "Oh, I'm sorry. I just thought it might be helpful."

Mary: "Hey, guess what. I'm stuck. I don't want you turning group members into parents who'll watch you and point out your baddies. And yet, right now, I am a parent pointing out your baddie in asking for that. Where do you and I go from here?"

Ann: "I don't know."

Mary: "Me neither."

In vocabulary, voice tone, and body posture, I continue to work with her, primarily in Adult-monitored Child, never from Parent. The patient then plays my role, is her own therapist, and eventually discovers the thrill of autonomy. She does not need a new set of parents.

Sometimes refusal to adapt in therapy may be in the service of the Free Child, and the unsuspecting therapist, in parenting, may punish the rebellion and discourage the patient's free spirit. For example, Joy told of a workshop in which she had refused to do what was expected of her as a patient, and the entire group including the therapist had wanted to punish her.

Bob: "Who's that therapist remind you of?"

Joy: "I don't know what you mean."

Mary: "Close your eyes. You are being told you don't do it right. You are told that you are *making* everyone uncomfortable. Stay with the scene until you ·know who that therapist reminds you of."

Joy *(after weeping)*: "My father spanked me because I forgot my lines in a school play. And all the kids hated me."

Bob: "Congratulations."

Joy: "What?"

Bob: "Congratulations for not letting that therapist punish you. For not letting him do what your father did."

Joy: *(laughing spontaneously—the first nondepressed sound she has made all week)*: "I am rather gutsy at times."

Bob: "Congratulations for protecting yourslf."

We set up a dialogue between her gutsy self and her depressed self, and she learned that her depressed self was also very frightened. She then offered herself protection from her gutsy side. With her decision to protect herself, she redecided to live and not to let anyone harm her. During the next few days she easily understood and discarded the "Kick Me" game she had used in the previous workshop, and, as a child, when she had forgotten her lines. It is always easier to give up games after a redecision.

A year later she attended an advanced workshop and reported that Bob's "Congratulations" had made a life or death difference for her; she had been contemplating suicide because she had felt she was in the same old place, until she was stroked (at a time when she was punishing herself) for not allowing herself to be punished by others.

Another example:

Joe: "I find myself hypercritical of myself in the job situation. Maybe I'm on a 'Don't succeed' trip. But I think it's more a 'Don't feel like you succeed.'"
(We ask the facts about his job and his performance on it. He has a good job and does it well.)
Mary: "Like your job?"
Joe: "I would if I could get off this thing I do to myself."
Mary: "Let's hear how you do it."
Joe: "You can't do this job. It's too demanding. You're not creative. You're just stumbling along."
(He fights back halfheartedly. We do some body work with him, to let him experience and change his shallow breathing and muscle tension. Then he dialogues between his right fist and his leg-stroking left hand. Later:)
Joe: *(talking from his clenched fist)*: "Why the hell don't I get off myself?"
Bob: "Answer that."
Joe: "I feel I don't know how. It's so much a part of me. I don't know how. I'd like to feel successful without having to pull the rug out—"
Mary: "When were you successful as a little kid?"
Joe: "I don't know. I—[*Pause.*] I led the Little League in batting."
Mary: "Did you feel successful?"
Joe: "As a batter?"
Mary: "Yeah."
Joe: "Not particulary."
Mary: "I imagine you struck out once."*(Laughter.)*
Joe: "I told myself a lot of my hits should have been caught."
(Loud laughter.)
Bob: "That's not funny."

Joe: "That's—that's what I thought. Jesus Christ, what a stupid thought. But I felt that way."
Bob: "What do you suppose would happen if you let yourself be proud of you?"
Joe: "I'd be stuck up."
Bob: "Maybe."
Joe: "I'd be proud and vain. Yeah, that was pretty strong. 'Don't speak highly of yourself.' Probably 'Do not even think highly of yourself.' My parents didn't think highly of themselves. 'You've got to be special and deny it the whole time.'"
Mary: "Are you willing to go back in time? Be there in your Little League days? Willing to be proud and vain?"
Joe: "Uh huh."
Mary *(standing)*: "Stand up and be the Little League batter. Be—what are you, 11 or 12?"
Joe *(hanging his head)*: "I guess about 10 maybe."
Mary: "Ten. Hey, you were young to lead the league."
Joe: "I was. [*Holds head up*] It was the first year I was in the league. I batted left-handed."
Bob: "Be there. Put your body and all of you into being proud."
Joe: "I'm glad. I almost never strike out. I can hit—I wasn't—I'm not a power hitter. I can really hit singles. And I—It was great."
Bob: "I'm great."
Joe: "That's something new. I'm great. I've never said that. I'm great. Wow! I am great! Yeah. I made my team come in first in the league. They couldn't have done it without me. [*He looks energized, and is smiling excitedly. His body is congruent, his voice has deepened.*] I hit the ball right between right and center!"
(Everbody applauds)

Who should be treated with redecision therapy? We have used it successfully with all who are not actively psychotic. A more important question is: Which therapists should use redecision therapy? The system looks deceptively easy, but it can be used in unconstructive and even dangerous ways. To practice successfully, the therapist needs to know psychopathology, and needs to be trained in gestalt techniques as well as in transactional analysis. Since redecisions are made by the Free Child, the technique is not appropriate in adaptive or psychoanalytic groups.

REFERENCES AND SUGGESTED READINGS

Barnes, G. (Ed.) *Transactional analysis after Eric Berne: Teaching and practice of three TA schools.* New York: Harper & Row, 1977.

Berne, E. *Transactional analysis in psychotherapy.* New York: Grove Press, 1961.

Berne, E. *The structure and dynamics of organizations and groups.* Philadelphia: Lippincott, 1963.

Berne, E. *Games people play.* New York: Grove Press, 1964.

Berne, E. *Principles of group treatment.* New York: Oxford University Press, 1966.

Berne, E. *Sex in human loving.* New York: Simon & Schuster, 1970.

Berne E. *What do you say after you say hello?* New York: Grove Press, 1972.

Berne, E. Four books on group therapy: A review. In M. Rosenbaum, & M. M. Berger (Eds.), *Group psychotherapy and group function.* New York: Basic Books, 1975.

Berne, E. *Intuition and ego states: The origins of transactional analysis.* San Francisco: TA Press, 1977.

Bunney, W. E., Jr., Fawcett, J. A., Davis, J. M., et al. Further evaluation of urinary 17-hydroxycorticosteroids in suicidal patients. *Archives of General Psychiatry,* 1969, *21,* 138-150.

Campos, L., & McCormick, P. *Introduce yourself to transactional analysis.* San Francisco: Transactional Publications, 1969.

Campos, L., & McCormick, P. *Introduce your marriage to transactional analysis.* San Francisco: Transactional Publications, 1972.

Crossman, P. Permission and protection. *Transactional Analysis Bulletin,* 1966, 5 (19), 152-154.

DeVos, G. A. Suicide in cross-cultural perspective. In H.L.P. Resnik (Ed.), *Suicidal behaviors*. Boston: Little, Brown, 1968.

Dusay, J. *Egograms*. New York: Harper & Row, 1977.

English, F. Episcript and the "Hot Potato" game. *Transactional Analysis Bulletin*, 1969, 8(32), 77-82.

Ernst, K. *Games students play (and what to do about them)*. Millbrae, California: Celestial Arts, 1972.

Fagan, J., & Shepherd, I. L. (Eds.). *Gestalt therapy now*. New York: Harper/Colophon, 1971.

Fawcett, J., Leff, M., & Bunney, W. E., Jr. Suicide clues from interpersonal communication. *Archives of General Psychiatry*, 1969, *21*, 129-137.

Gazda, G. M. (Ed.). *Basic approaches to group psychotherapy and group counseling*. Springfield, Ill.: Charles C. Thomas, 1975.

Goulding, R. L. Four models of transactional analysis. *International Journal of Group Psychotherapy*, 1976, *26*(3), 385-392.

Haimowitz, M. L., & Haimowitz, N. (Eds.). *Human development: Selected readings*. New York: Crowell, 1973.

Harris, J. R., & Meyers, J. M. Hospital management of the suicidal patient. In H.L.P. Resnik (Ed.), *Suicidal behaviors*. Boston: Little, Brown, 1968.

Hatcher, C., & Himelstein, P. (Eds.). *Handbook of gestalt therapy*. New York: Jason Aronson, 1976.

James, M., et al. *Techniques in transactional analysis*. Reading, Mass.: Addison-Wesley, 1977.

James, M., & Jongeward, D. *Born to win*. Reading, Mass.: Addison-Wesley, 1971.

Karpman, S. Fairy tales and script drama analysis. *Transactional Analysis Bulletin*, 1968, *7*(26), 39-43.

Lieberman, M. A., Yalom, I. D., & Miles, M. B. *En-*

counter groups: First facts. New York: Basic Books, 1973.

McCormick, P. *Guide for use of a life script questionnaire.* San Francisco: Transactional Publications, 1971.

McCormick, P. TA and behavior modification: A comparison study. *Transactional Analysis Journal,* 1973, 3 (1), 10-14.

McCormick, P. *Ego states.* San Francisco: Transactional Publications, 1977.

McCormick, P. *Social transactions.* San Francisco: Transactional Publications, 1977.

McNeel, J. *Redecisions in psychotherapy: A study of the effects of an intensive weekend group workshop.* Unpublished doctoral dissertation, The California School of Professional Psychology, 1975.

Perls, F. *Gestalt therapy verbatim.* Lafayette, California: Real People Press, 1969.

Perls, F. *In and out of the garbage pail.* Lafayette, California: Real People Press, 1969.

Polster, E., & Polster, M. *Gestalt therapy integrated.* New York: Brunner/Mazell, 1973.

Rosenbaum, M., & Berger, M. M. (Eds). *Group psychotherapy and group function.* New York: Basic Books, 1975.

Roth, S. The seemingly ubiquitous depression following acute schizophrenic episodes, a neglected area of clinical discussion. *American Journal of Psychiatry,* 1970, *127,* 51-58.

Sager, C. J., & Kaplan, H. S. (Eds.). *Progress in group and family therapy.* New York: Brunner/Mazel, 1972.

Satir, V. *Conjoint family therapy.* Palo Alto: Science and Behavior Books, 1964.

Satir, V. *Peoplemaking.* Palo Alto: Science and Behavior Books, 1972.

Schiff, J. Reparenting schizophrenics. *Transactional Analysis Bulletin*, 1969, 8(31), 47-63.

Schiff, J. L., & Day, B. *All my children*. Philadelphia: Lippincott, 1970.

Shein, H. M., & Stone, A. A. Monitoring and treatment of suicidal potential within the context of psychotherapy. *Comparative Psychiatry*, 1969, 10, 59-70.

Shneidman, E. S. Orientations toward death: A vital aspect of the study of lives. In H. L. P. Resnik (Ed.), *Suicidal behaviors*. Boston: Little, Brown, 1968.

Simkin, J. S. The use of dreams in gestalt therapy. In C. J. Sager & H. S. Kaplan (Eds.), *Progress in group and family therapy*. New York: Brunner/Mazel, 1972.

Steiner, C. Script and counterscript. *Transactional Analysis Bulletin*, 1966, 5(18), 133-135.

Steiner, C. A script checklist. *Transactional Analysis Bulletin*, 1967, 6(22), 38-39.

Transactional Analysis Bulletin: Selected articles (1962-1969). San Francisco: TA Press, 1976.

Transactional Analysis Journal. San Francisco: International Transactional Analysis Association. 1970-

Tuckman, J., & Youngman, W. F. Assessment of suicide risk in attempted suicides. In H. L. P. Resnik (Ed.), *Suicidal behaviors*. Boston: Little, Brown, 1968.

Voices: Journal of the American Academy of Psychotherapists. Orlando, Florida.

Wolpe, J. *The practice of behavior therapy*. New York: Pergamon, 1969.

Index